Stories About Penises

An anthology of short stories & poems

Edited by Julianne Ingles

guts publishing

"The penis does not obey the order of its master, who tries to erect or shrink it at will, whereas instead the penis erects freely while its master is asleep. The penis must be said to have its own mind."

Leonardo da Vinci

CONTENTS

Editor's Note	Julianne Ingles	1
Proclamation (p)	Matt Dennison	3
He (f)	Gerry Marsh	4
Wild Ideas (f)	Catherine Edmunds	8
Too Much Tea (nf)	Ann Rawson	22
My Gilly & Me (nf)	Adem Ay	34
Better Babies (f)	Liam Hogan	40
How I Lost My Virginity in a Lobster Trap (f)	Alex Carrigan	48
Dicks (f)	Gayelene Carbis	57
Two Doves (f)	Christina Lovin	60
Slip of a Knife (f)	Thaddeus Rutkowski	72
The Camera-Shy Cock (nf)	Edward Apeldoorn	74
Garden of Vaginas (f)	Shringi Kumari	84
Scratching the Surface (f)	Sarah Evans	93
Field (f)	Molly McLellan	104
Homage (nf)	Tobsha Learner	117
The Violinist at the Pulitzer Reading (p)	Anthony DiPietro	127
A Hard Look (p)	Benton Lenz	129
Sonnet 6" (p)	Drew Pisarra	131
The Clinical Cock (nf)	Thom Schwarz	132
We're So Sorry (nf)	Julianne Ingles	137
Too Many to Count (p)	Kathleen A Lawrence	148
Contributors		153
Individual Titles & Copyrights		161

EDITOR'S NOTE

Whose idea was this penis anthology? I must admit, it was mine. Yet I had no idea the Pandora's box that would open when I put out the open call for submissions. What started as a reaction to my own penis encounter became something much larger and broader than I ever imagined. The range of takes on the humble penis (which one of the writers said – *Julianne, that's an oxymoron!*) is staggering, from light and humorous to dead serious to heartbreaking.

This book is a collection of 21 poems & short stories (fiction and nonfiction) written by a talented group of writers from around the world. Thoughtfully selected work, some are tragic, some full-on, some comic, some bizarre and some of course erotic. It's an eclectic mix that will no doubt surprise you.

A huge sincere heartfelt thank you to all of the writers – I love each and every one of your stories and poems, and am honored to have them in this anthology. A delicate, controversial topic hit from every possible angle, with artistry.

The creation of this anthology was by no means a one-woman show. My sincere thanks to Laurie Martinez and Charlie Mars for hours of reading, feedback and support. Many thanks also to George Huxley for his help early on in this project, and for showing me the ropes on Instagram. Many thanks as well to Nate Ragolia (Spaceboy Books) for his patience and hand-holding through every stage of this project, for putting up with my numerous freak outs – *But Nate, the barcode, it's, it's covering part of the banana! Don't worry Julianne, it's all gonna be fine.* And an enormous thank you to Goldsmiths College, for without their support I'm not sure any of this would have happened.

I hope you enjoy these stories and poems as much as I have. They are a mix of fiction and nonfiction. On the Contents page, each title is labeled as (*f*) fiction, (*nf*) nonfiction, and (*p*) poem.

Julianne Ingles
25 September 2019

MATT DENNISON
Proclamation

I woke, I pissed, I had a cum—
my dick's been good to me.

Though you could say that it's the one
to blame for everything.

GERRY MARSH
He

The hard smack of a van over the sleeping policeman had woken him. He hears it accelerate away, as headlights from another car search the far wall of their bedroom. As if their terraced home were a porous thing. He stares at the ceiling and wonders what time it is, but doesn't check the clock. He thinks about the cars. How their home is on the rat run and by early morning the traffic hums as it backs up outside. He imagines the waiting drivers staring at his shut blinds. His home it appears is not a destination, but a place that's passed on the way to somewhere better.

He closes his eyes and pushes back the duvet a bit, yearns to shuck the whole thing off with his feet and let it fall, but fears it will wake her. The questions would start then. What's the matter? Are you alright?

Instead he gets his knob out and holds it.

No cars pass and quietness falls. He thought he might fancy a wank but he just holds it and stares at the cobwebs in the corners of the ceiling. It needs a coat of paint 'cause there hadn't been enough time to do a decent job.

He forgets his sleeping knob as his insomniac mind extends to the loft above. Bearing down on him is the sheer weight of accumulated objects. He thinks about Jay's cot folded away in the recesses of the eaves, resting next to the baby bottle steriliser around which so many of his early parental rituals revolved. Then there was the baby walker surrounded by sacks of early-years toys and educational aids. And old mattresses that should have been chucked, but he never had time. Suitcases that were going nowhere. The thought provokes an anxiety akin to excitement and his knob stirs.

He gives his dick a pull or two but it turns over and goes back to sleep.

He pushes against the duvet again, only to discover it's fallen away to reveal his splayed legs and gap in his boxers where his thing hangs out.

He wants a release and wishes he could give this to himself. Yet it's like he's still suffocating under the weight of the duvet. Or the weight of discarded marital detritus in the attic above. Old music collections, soiled rugs, her books, his stereo. He squeezes his eyes shut and tries to let go of the weight and think about boobs instead. Big ones. Jugs. He turns slowly onto his side, aware of her back. Jugs. Big ones. Nope, it's not happening, and behind his lids the powerhouse of his brain belts out trivia loudly.

He is sinking, through the floor, like a ghost haunting his own home. Floating through the new 'Family Kitchen/Diner'. He'd opened his doors to a bunch of builders and asked them to give him a 'Family' Kitchen/Diner. Because that's what families had to have. Spotlighting and dishwashers and easy close drawers. So they'd smashed the little kitchen wall down, cloaked the house in brick dust, broke pictures, hoovered wet plaster up, poured glutinous stuff down drains, swore, shouted, smoked, spat, and loafed around, till finally their job was done. Any residual desire to be in his family home was beaten out of him over those months fulfilling an out of date dream. When they finally left, one wall was down and another was up permanently. If something breaks now, he mends it, or learns how to.

No. Come on. He leaves it broke.

There were a lot of broken things in his home.

His dick for one. Inoperative. Kaput. Busted. No, no he could do this. He thinks of Sonia at work. Her breasts hanging out. Bending over. Please God, he could give himself a little pleasure even if life was shit. Couldn't he?

He looks down, his spirit disinterested in reviving the corpse of his penis. His mind sinks into the downstairs hallway, as if waiting for permission to leave. He stares at yesterday's junk mail gathering on the rug. He can't stop the stuff arriving. Leaflets scream their messages at him '50% Sale on Soffits and Guttering', 'Tree Surgeon – Bring Light into Your Home', 'Double Glazing, Nothing to Pay till August 2019'. Inadequate salves to improve his deficient home. His letterbox a hungry mouth that he would love to stop up with old newspaper if he were only allowed. And stick up a sign that said: 'No junk mail. No mail. No callers. No demands, no nothing, just go away and leave me the hell alone why don't you.'

A façade then this home. A lie to please his daughter, whilst he waits out his prison stretch.

He puts his dick away and covers over the gap in his boxers. It doesn't matter. It's just a flop of organ.

He thinks instead of her, his reason for staying. His only daughter, Jay, his warm hearth. The hallway adorned with her abandoned shoes, the dining room chair enrobed with her blazer, the table glittering with elastic bands, felt tip lids, sweet wrappers and all manner of glorious detritus, the squeals from sleepovers temporarily magnifying this terraced shell as he serves out his sentence, fills the void and attends to the fiction, plays the illusionist and creates something more than is actually there. Decorating the tree at Christmas, carving the pumpkins at Halloween, putting out the mince pie and carrot for Rudolf.

Illusion or substance. It felt real. Wasn't that what husbandry was? Caring for, nurturing and allowing to grow? He weighed up the equation – his feeble dick versus that moment of potency seven years ago. Okay. Was it okay being absent and present?

Outside, a car slows down and sweeps its lights across the wall. He watches and forgets his thoughts. As the darkness reasserts itself a monstrous notion takes shape, sits in the shadows and stares back at him. No, dear God. His little girl would one day grow up and leave this home. What would happen to them? To him?

He curls tighter and searches for the duvet, floating somewhere between sleep and wakefulness, not quite able to grasp something out of reach. What would life be like for him, he thinks, freed from this in-between place? No longer a suitcase in the attic.

CATHERINE EDMUNDS
Wild Ideas

Jolyon was lost again. He propped his bicycle against an ash tree, sat down on the grassy bank, looking vaguely around for wild eglantine, and opened Cicely's map. Her letter fell out, the one in which she had written of a strange experience on an aeroplane. They hadn't corresponded since, but he had kept the letter close, taking it out at every ten minutes to read it and try to understand. After a week of worry, he had folded the delicate sheet of notepaper and slipped it into the map case to take with him on his tour of the Northern Pennines, the expectation being that once in the bracing air he would have an epiphany, he would go back to London, they would laugh at his confusion, and—he wasn't entirely sure what followed.

Jolyon couldn't imagine Cicely in an aeroplane. She lived quietly in a modest set of rooms behind the Bayswater Road and rarely ventured further than Lancaster Gate, though on a sunny afternoon she would sometimes take a turn in Hyde Park, accompanied by Roberts, her maid. Yet here was this letter, this slip of a thing, full of wild ideas. Some of it was sensible. She advised him to wear certain socks which she believed would protect his feet from blisters; she passed on sound advice from Roberts regarding the purchase of a Harris Tweed cap, and the best tailor to approach for a pair of plus fours. They had agreed on the need for string in case he lost his cycle clips. He remembered sitting in Cicely's parlour while she and Roberts giggled about the string, which he'd thought most forward of Roberts, but who was he to complain about Cicely's arrangements? It was not his province, and he knew nothing of such things anyway.

The fantastical aeroplane incident had been bad enough, but it had been followed in the very next paragraph by the bald announcement that she was pregnant. When he read those words the first time, at his club, he had exclaimed, and half risen from his chair. Simpkins had brought him a large brandy and he had recovered soon enough, but whatever had put such an absurd thought into her head? He was not entirely *au fait* with what he liked to call 'family matters', but he was certain the decorous peck on the cheek with which he habitually greeted her could not possibly have caused her to become with child. To do that would have required the insertion of his penis into the part of her anatomy that connected with her womb. The doctor had explained to him how this worked. He was aware of the workings of his penis anyway, having been public school educated, but he was sure he would have noticed if he'd inserted his penis into Cicely. Yet there it was, there was the thing she had written. He had never previously noticed any signs of hysteria in her.

Amongst the long moors and small wooded valleys, it all seemed impossibly, and thankfully, distant. He closed his eyes and lay back. The sun beat down and the scent of honeysuckle assailed his nostrils in a most pleasant way. A bird called with an eerie, chirring cry. He believed it to be a curlew, and felt proud of his knowledge, but there was something mournful about its call. He had yet to approach Cicely formally, but now, he was experiencing something that if it were not so ridiculous, he would call 'fear'. How much of an understanding did he and Cicely really have? He wasn't sure, but he knew breach of promise was a serious matter. People fought duels. Perhaps this was caused by his reluctance to take matters further. Had he unwittingly caused her to go insane? Should he have utilised his penis's properties, even before the wedding night? He had visions of Bedlam, and shivered, but the sky was as bright as ever, mocking him. He opened the letter and read again: *I have held in all but one tear, and that one is for you.*

At first he thought this meant she'd been weeping for him, but now, as he read the words more carefully, he realised what they really said. What a confounded thing! Her words meant she had only shed one tear for him. One! That was all he was worth. He folded the letter and slipped it back into the map which he secured in his haversack. He had an urge to race his bicycle pell-mell across the moors, but a tyre would burst, and he was foolish in such matters with no idea how he might effect a repair. Best to stick to sensible roads with small villages within walking distance. Just one tear? Oh, Cicely.

Cicely... Cicely... rising from her dressing table, her hair shining, a small smile quivering on her lips, raising a finger and whispering, "Wait till the evening," and he, wondering at being so blessed, at having this creature, this Cicely, looking up at him demurely as if awaiting permission—but then this awful fear, which in a woman would be 'nerves'; his stuttering, unsure of the correct words, the shrug of her shoulders as she turned away to pick up the map with the words, "Perhaps you should go on that cycle tour," and he, nonplussed, not having mentioned any such idea thinking, yes! A cycle tour! What a tremendous idea! And Roberts scuttling away—did she laugh? Now he was sure; the maid had been laughing at him.

He picked up the bicycle and surveyed the view, which went on forever, and the clouds, distant and thunderous, but shedding their precipitation no doubt over the mighty fells of the Lake District, far enough away not to worry him. He would cycle on, he would reach Hartside Summit, he would write to Cicely and tell her about the view. She would like that. He would hint that perhaps Roberts could be given her notice.

But even as he had the thought, he knew the letter would remain unwritten. An aeroplane! Had she been whisked away to the coast by some ne'er do well, and taken on a perilous flight across the channel? Had she arrived in France and sipped absinthe with dangerous artists? He had heard of such things. Had one of them kissed her, not just on the cheek—had one of them dared touch her lips? Had there been more? Had there been a penis insertion? He flushed. He didn't know what he meant by that, not really. It seemed so unlikely, but even thinking about it was causing his organ to engorge a little.

Hard work, that's what he needed. He mounted his bicycle, despite the temporary awkwardness, and pedalled up the road. The wind was against him, but he fought it, soon out of breath, aching with the effort. He passed a snake of men, coal-blackened, who stared at him as if he were something monstrous and strange, and he thought, perhaps he was, perhaps he had no right to be here. There were lights in the distance, perhaps a small chapel. That would be his goal. The clouds, which had seemed so far away moments earlier, crowded the sky. The bicycle had no lamps. This was unsafe. He stopped. The summit was too far away. Cicely was too far away. He was beastly cold.

The rain fell with great heavy drops. He remembered

Roberts telling him that Harris Tweed was sovereign against a shower. He should have spoken then, should have dismissed Roberts for her impertinence, should have asked Cicely for her hand. He hadn't, and now she had toppled into insanity, shedding only one tear for him. She was consorting with Frenchmen, she had embraced a French penis, and now she was with child. She had sent him away on a bicycle, and he had never even kissed her lips.

The blackened men tramped past him, a never-ending line, hurrying back to those rows of cottages with the smoke rising from the chimneys. They had wives, perhaps children. The rain poured down and Jolyon threw his bicycle into a ditch and the accursed Harris Tweed cap after it. He would catch pneumonia and die, and then perhaps she would deign to let the other tears flow. He scrabbled in his haversack for the map. Her letter dropped out onto the ground and the rain dissolved the writing. He tramped on in the direction of the chapel. There were sighs, voices, chaotic angels singing through the storm, calling him.

* * *

My dearest Jolyon,

Do you know what it is to fly? To be airborne, to let loose the bonds that tie you to the ground? I have had an adventure, unparalleled and fantastical, but I can see you shaking your head, and thinking about aeroplanes. Oh, my darling, sometimes I feel so sorry for you. But you have your trip coming up, you have something lovely to look forward to, and Roberts assures me those northern fells will blow the cobwebs away. You have your bicycle. I have the sky, the air, the heavens!

Roberts peered over Cicely's shoulder and read what she had written so far.

"He really will think you're talking about aeroplanes, won't he."

Cicely put down her pen and didn't speak. Roberts put her hands on her mistress' shoulders and leaned over to kiss the top of her head. "I know—tell him you're pregnant."

Cicely covered her mouth to stifle the laugh, then picked up her pen, and wrote, *I'm pregnant.*

"Golly," she said.

The two women stared at the words.

"You would be if I were the footman rather than the maid," said Roberts, quietly.

"I can't leave it like that. Whatever will he think?"

"I don't know. Does he think? I've never seen any evidence."

"Don't be mean. I know: *I have held in all but one tear, and that one is for you.* There. He'll understand that I've saved the best, the most special tear for him. I owe him that at least."

"You don't owe him anything."

"He's been kind."

"Haven't I?"

"More than kind."

Cicely took Roberts' hand in her own and kissed it. "Now I must finish this." She took up her pen again. The rest of the letter was standard fare. She mentioned birds, the old lady who fed the ducks on the Serpentine, a beautiful sunset. The words trailed away saying nothing at all and ended with a wish that he would enjoy his bicycle tour and return full of tales of the wonders he had seen.

She read it through and came close to screwing it up

and throwing it away, but Roberts took it from her, folded it carefully, dabbed on a little of Cicely's perfume, and took it away.

Cicely stared at her three-angled reflection in the dressing table mirror. She imagined Jolyon; tall, elegant, beautiful Jolyon, coming up behind her and smiling with that timidity she had found so beguiling at first. When he returned she would explain away the pregnancy. He would believe any nonsense. They would marry, she would take Roberts with her as her personal maid, Jolyon would raise no objection. They could have a perfectly pleasant life together.

Pleasant. Oh…!

Roberts came in ten minutes later, to find her mistress lying on the bed sobbing. She lit the lamps and drew the curtains, then crept away. She would tell Cook to warm up a dish of broth. Task done, she climbed the stairs to her own little room, lit the fire, pulled a blanket round her shoulders and sat on the bed. Cicely's tears were infectious. That silly, silly man. She hoped he would lose his way, she hoped his bicycle's front forks would buckle beyond repair, she hoped he would fall down a mine shaft. If he came back, she would be dismissed, she felt it in her bones. She shivered and put another piece of coal on the fire.

* * *

Laura Teasdale wrapped the muffler round her neck, took hold of her daughter's hand and set off from the little chapel for the two-mile walk back to her cottage for the last time. She had no money left for the rent. The seven and sixpence compensation for Stanley's death had run out quickly, and the generosity of her neighbours couldn't go on any longer. It would be the workhouse for her and Jenny. But this last time, she would enjoy the walk, she wouldn't let her daughter have her memories of this place sullied. If only it hadn't been raining. She would have loved to have seen the view down the dale in sunshine, glistening and fresh.

They had barely gone two hundred yards when Jenny pulled on her arm and pointed to the ditch at the side of the road.

"What's that, Mama? I want to look. Can I go and look?"

Laura could see a dark bundle and tried to make out a dead sheep through the pouring rain, but it was the wrong shape. She followed her daughter and was shocked to discover a man's body in waterlogged clothes. She told Jenny to stand very still and not come too close while Mama saw if the man was poorly.

His cheek was cold, but she found a faint pulse in his neck. There was no smell of alcohol, and he certainly wasn't local. His dress was extraordinary. She stood up, took her daughter's hand again, and said the man had taken bad, so they had best go tell Mr Hunter. They tramped back towards the chapel.

"Mrs Teasdale—I was just locking up. Did you leave anything?"

"No, I don't think so, but we have found a gentleman who appears to have met with some kind of an accident."

"He's fallen in the ditch," said Jenny.

"Oh," said Mr Hunter, the disapproval evident on his face.

"He has hurt himself. We should help him," said Mrs Teasdale, staring straight at the minister.

15

"Of course, of course. I'll come and take a look, shall I? You lead the way, young lady."

Jenny skipped on ahead, reached the spot, and stood proudly pointing at her discovery.

"Well, well," said the minister. He seemed reluctant to do anything else.

"Can we take him home and make him better?" said Jenny.

"A splendid idea. Your mother can nurse him back to health. You go on ahead, Mrs Teasdale, and I'll get Dan and Jeb to carry him down to your cottage. We'll get Dr Clay to call and tell you what needs doing."

"Mr Hunter, I can't afford the doctor."

"Then let's see if the young gentleman can."

The minister knelt down and rummaged in Jolyon's jacket. He drew out his pocketbook with a flourish, opened it, and handed it to Laura. She had never held so much money in her entire life.

"You take good care of that. He'll be grateful."

Laura looked Mr Hunter in the eye until he was forced to turn away.

"I'll go ahead and put some water on the hob," she said eventually.

"Good, good. I'll organise transport for this poor chap."

He walked away briskly, leaving Laura holding enough money to buy fuel to see her through any number of winters, shoes for Jenny, a warm coat, and as much food as they could eat.

On the way back to the cottage she wondered what Stanley would have made of it all. What if this man died too? No, he mustn't. Her mind raced on ahead. She would nurse him back to health, he would stay and be a new daddy for Jenny, he would take care of them and they would be happy again. Never mind that he was a gentleman, who no doubt lived in a mansion with twenty servants. Never mind he would certainly have a wife, a family. She hurried on, Jenny skipping along beside her.

The cottage was icy, but Laura thought of all the money and built up a fire, put a pot to boil with some barley and carrots and a whole onion, plus two of the precious peppercorns and a pinch of salt. A warming bowl of broth would do them all good. She arranged some blankets and a bolster on the settle and sat down to wait, while Jenny played happily with her peg dolls.

Half an hour later, the men brought the gentleman in. They laid him carefully on the settle, but refused a bowl of broth and left quickly—they both had wives who would be suspicious if they spent too much time with the pretty young widow.

"He's very wet," said Jenny.

"We'll have to do something about that, won't we."

"Are you going to take his clothes off?"

"I think I'll have to. Let's fetch some more blankets, and then you'd best go upstairs until I've finished."

Jenny brought the blankets, glad to be useful, then climbed the ladder to the cottage's tiny attic bedroom.

Laura drew the curtains and lit the candle in the mirrored alcove. Its warm light flickered across the room. The gentleman looked absurdly young, and very beautiful. She hardly dared touch him, but he was soaking and freezing, and she had seen tuberculosis and pneumonia often enough to know she had to get him warm and dry as quickly as possible. She stripped off his clothes, wondering at the weave and the softness of his undergarments. Beneath, he looked like a marble statue. She stood looking at him for a while, comparing him to her Stanley, a stocky and well-muscled man, built like an ox above but a poodle below. This gentleman was different. He was like a statue, but not those ancient ones she'd once seen in a museum with the tiny penises that had made her giggle. No, this gentleman was perfect. His breathing was slow and steady, so she risked reaching out and touching. He didn't stir. She cradled the penis in her hand, and it was warm and quiescent. It was impossible not to imagine how it could be if aroused. There was a slight stirring, and she took her hand away quickly, tucked the blankets around him and willed him to be warm, to recover. And most of all to be kind. She ached for some kindness and he was so very beautiful. All of him.

* * *

Cicely had been ill, feverish and hallucinating; for a while she really believed she was pregnant, she fancied she'd flown to Paris and been ravished by a man with garlic breath and bad teeth, and a revolting penis like an engorged worm, and now she was terrified she was going to give birth to a string of onions. Then one morning the fever broke and she told Roberts about her wild fancies and Roberts burst out in peals of laughter. Cicely wanted to be cross, but she couldn't, and soon she was giggling herself, but then she was coughing badly, and Roberts stopped laughing and held her until the coughing fit passed.

She lay back on her pillows.

"How long have I been ill?"

"A week. I've been frightened."

"You? Frightened? Oh, love. What, did I turn into a gargoyle? Was I entirely hideous?"

"You were like a ghost."

"I'll get better now. Promise. But I can't talk much. It hurts my chest."

"Do you think you could fancy a little broth?"

"Yes, I really think I could."

Roberts went to the kitchen and heated up the broth as she'd done every day for the last week in the hope that Cicely might manage some. Every evening she'd sipped a little herself and then thrown the rest away. Every morning, as Cook had shaken her head, she had made some fresh. Every day Cicely had looked paler, apart from two bright spots on her cheeks, like a badly painted doll. The doctor had visited frequently and let blood, and tutted, and talked about time, and not to worry, and the crisis must come soon, and they were just words, but they'd kept her going—and he'd been right.

She took the bowl of broth up on a tray with a clean napkin and some sprigs of lavender tied together with a purple ribbon.

"Oh, Roberts, how lovely! Talk to me, please talk to me."

"What about?"

"Anything."

Cicely sat back against the pillows and waited.

"There was a lovely little toy the children had at my last place," said Roberts. "A Noah's ark set."

"I used to have one of those."

"What were the lions like?"

"The lions?" Cicely furrowed her brow. "They were

19

like lions." She took another sip of broth.

"Manes?"

"Yes, of course."

"Both of them?"

"Yes. Oh!"

"Exactly."

"We're going to be okay, aren't we."

"Yes. We are. But... there's a letter. I haven't opened it."

Cicely drank some more of her broth. "This is delicious."

"Don't you want to see the letter?"

"Yes. Your lovely broth is doing its work and making me strong. Please read it to me."

Roberts opened the envelope and took a deep breath.

My Dearest Cicely,

I find myself in a strange situation. I am thinking of your last letter—which alas, I no longer have in my possession—and I think I understand now about the aeroplane, because I have been flying myself. The doctor says I was lucky, that I suffered some kind of 'brain storm' but was found soon enough, with the result that the after-effects have been no more serious than a slight chill. I am young and strong, and the doctor says of course I have been receiving the best possible care, and that is what has done the trick.

I hope you and—how can I put this? Your condition. I hope your condition is what you would wish it to be, whatever that might be. In fact, I rather think I understand, because I find I have unexpectedly given birth in a manner of speaking myself. Whatever the cause, I seem to be a father of a six-year-old child, and she is delightful, she is called Jenny and she has two peg dolls which the minister told her to call Verity and Truth—I suggested we call them Flossie and Abigail instead, and do you know, she ran up and gave me a hug when I said that, and her mother laughed and I was so happy. Cicely, you must understand this and not be offended. I realised I had never known true joy before.

I love you and I will always love you, but we both know your fondness for me was a gentle and sweet thing, it was never going to be enough. You will not, I'm sure, be hurt when I say I don't intend to make you a formal offer. I am sure we both wish to be free to make our own choices, however unlikely to the rest of the world and to society at large, those choices might be.

Ever your affectionate friend,
Jolyon

"Oh, the sweet, sweet man," said Roberts. "Do you think he really means it?"

Cicely leaned back on her pillows and closed her eyes. "Yes, no question," she said. "And what is more, I'm not going to have to..."

"Oh, yes. Yuck. You won't have to touch that—that *thing.*"

21

ANN RAWSON
Too Much Tea

Bedsit Land, January 1982

I'm standing in the middle of an unfamiliar room. It's a cold room, even though I've put fifty pence of my own in the meter and turned the electric fire on. I'm twenty-two and I'm the most embarrassed I've ever been.

The room is shabbily furnished, with a couple of tatty armchairs, an ugly oak wardrobe and a big, old chest of drawers. A single bed, half-hidden behind a screen, is neatly made, hospital corners, with a pile of folded blankets on the end. On one side of the window there's a tiny sink unit and a white painted cupboard with a two-ring hob and a kettle. On the other, there's a yellow Formica table with two mismatched wooden dining chairs.

A third wooden chair is in front of me. I've put a plastic washing up bowl on it, for want of anything better. Standing next to me, leaning on me, with one arm around my shoulder, and his other hand grasping the back of the wooden chair, is Mr Hatchard, one of my neighbours.

Mr Hatchard is ex-military, traditionally stiff-upper-lipped, always bolt upright, with a shock of white hair and piercing blue eyes. He has one of his blankets draped around his shoulders, but he's still shivering.

He's in a lot of pain. He's fallen in the street and broken his leg, or maybe his hip.

'I'm sorry,' he says, in his cut glass accent. 'I need your help. If I let go of the chair I'll fall again. I don't want to miss.'

Oh God, oh God, oh God. I have to direct his aim.

It's either that or clean it up afterwards.

The poor man. He's probably more embarrassed than I am. He hates asking for help. He was apologetic enough earlier when he was dumped unceremoniously on the front doorstep by the man who'd knocked him over when he was crossing the high street, where the fresh snow had fallen on compacted ice.

'It's okay,' I say. 'I think we can manage this, between us.'

I smile but avoid catching his eye as I undo the button on his trousers. I stifle an inappropriate laugh. He must be, what, in his seventies?

It will be the oldest penis I've seen. The oldest penis I've ever touched.

Everything about him is immaculate, thank God. His trousers beautifully pressed. A clean white shirt. A tie – just to go to the shops. His lace up black shoes are polished to a mirror finish that has survived the morning's disaster.

I fumble with the zip and it's fine, his trousers fall open to reveal perfectly white Y fronts.

I gently push the fabric to one side and find his penis with my hand. It's soft and pale and much like every penis I've ever seen, only with a sagging scrotum and sparse pubic hair. I grasp his penis. I try not to look more than the minimum necessary, but I can feel it. Like a little bird, trembling in my hand.

I pull the chair and the bowl closer, and he stumbles a little but it's fine, and I take aim. I hope my aim is good enough. It's not something I've ever done before. I've helped drunk ex-boyfriends who were throwing up, held back their long hair, and aimed them at the toilet bowl. I've cleaned them up and put them to bed. They might not have had perfect aim but they never needed this kind of help.

'I'm sorry,' he says. 'I'm desperate but I can't relax.'

'It's fine,' I lie. 'We've got ages before the doctor will arrive.'

If only I'd not done as I was told and kept him hydrated. All those cups of tea I'd made.

Eventually there's a tinkle. A few drops, then suddenly, like a dam breaking, a steady stream of urine soars from the penis in my hand into the bowl. A few drips might have missed, but we did it. We did fine. Teamwork.

I grab the wad of toilet roll I'd placed ready and dab the end of his penis dry.

It's not that different to a young penis. He's not circumcised. It's still got that lovely smooth velvety skin which is so soft to touch.

Oh God, why did my mind go there? This is embarrassing enough already without me thinking about sex. Perhaps he is too? I'm blushing now; my cheeks red hot.

I quickly put his dry penis back into his pants and zip him and button him up without looking up. I settle him briskly back into the armchair, and he yelps a little with the pain. I know that means he's hurting a lot. He hates needing help.

'I'll just go dispose of this lot,' I say, breezily. I keep my back to him – I don't want him to see I'm still blushing. I wipe the few drips up from the chair on a bit more toilet roll, then I rush out of the door with the sloshing bowl and down the corridor to the communal bathroom. Luckily there's no one in there. I lock the door behind me and

24

quickly empty the bowl down the loo and rinse it out in the bath. I dry it with yet more toilet paper.

Finally I put the loo seat down, sit and relax for a moment. Now I can let myself laugh.

I could never, ever handle being a nurse.

Back in his room, I reassure him that I've washed his bowl properly and put it back by his little sink unit.

I manage to look him in the eye without blushing. Without thinking, I ask him if he'd like another cup of tea.

He barks out a hearty laugh, and I blush, but I laugh too.

'Better not, perhaps,' he says, when he stops laughing.

'I know,' I say. 'I wish the doctor would hurry up. I know you're hungry, but they did say not to let you eat.'

'I'm sorry,' he says, not for the first time. 'I should have let that young man take me to hospital. I wanted to believe I could manage, but...'

'It's alright,' I say. 'I understand.'

The driver of the car he'd walked into on the snowy high street – he'd known better though. He'd had a choice. It was simply quicker and easier to drop Mr Hatchard back home than to take him to the nearest Casualty, where no doubt he'd have been questioned about the accident.

There was probably a legal duty to report it.

Lucky for Mr Hatchard I'd been in. If it hadn't been snowing, I'd have been down at Claremont Road, cleaning Mrs Banerjee's other properties and collecting the meter money and the rent from her other tenants. Instead, I'd been polishing the tiled hallway and singing along to the radio when the doorbell had interrupted me. I'd gone to sleep with the Pretenders and found my way home with Jon and Vangelis. When I opened the door the Birdie Song came on and formed the most inappropriate soundtrack as I talked to the driver.

'You should have taken him to hospital,' I said.

'He didn't want to go,' the baby-faced young man said. I believed that part of his story.

'He's one of your residents,' he went on. 'He's your responsibility now.'

'I just live here,' I said. 'In the back bedsit.'

The driver looked at me with the floor polisher and ignored what I said. He thought I was lying, or he didn't care.

I looked at Mr Hatchard who had his eyes closed with pain, waiting for him to back me up.

'At least help me get him upstairs to his room,' I said. But the driver had gone.

I'd suggested to Mr Hatchard that he could sit in my room, which was on the ground floor, while we decided what to do next, but he was determined to get to his own room. Somehow, with him hanging on to the bannister I'd just polished on his left, and with his right arm draped around my shoulder, we made it to his door.

I opened up with the passkey and helped him into his armchair. He finally groaned with pain and I realised that in spite of all his denials, he had probably broken something. His leg, or his hip.

He wouldn't let me call an ambulance, and anyway, the nearest telephone kiosk was only a few yards short of the doctor's surgery, so he agreed to let me go and arrange for his doctor to make a home visit.

We wait.

Every so often I run down the stairs to check the front door. I need to escape. It's a little tense and uncomfortable.

We can't find anything to say – we've long since exhausted the topic of the weather.

At last the doctor arrives. I take him up to Mr Hatchard's room explaining what happened. He laughs, saying there's no way we'd have made it upstairs if there was anything broken.

Five minutes later, with me waiting outside the room to give Mr Hatchard some privacy, the doctor calls me back into the room. He's not laughing any more. Mr Hatchard has a broken hip. It's a good thing he's not had anything to eat and he shouldn't have anything else to drink while we wait for the ambulance. Mr Hatchard manages a rather strangled sounding laugh.

The ambulance arrives surprisingly quickly. I say goodbye to Mr Hatchard and wish him good luck. He asks me to explain to our landlady Mrs Banerjee that he will pay all the rent later and insists that I tell her he will be coming back as soon as he can.

'I don't want to stay in hospital, and I don't want to go into a home,' he says, over and over. I promise I'll tell her.

Two weeks later, early on Saturday morning, there's a knock at the back door of our flat. It can only be Mrs Banerjee. No one else comes to that door.

It seems ironic that we moved here because Ryan's mother had a habit of walking into our room at six in the morning to wake us up to go to the garden centre or do some digging.

'Come in,' I call, and she uses her passkey.

'I'm sorry,' she says, sounding not very sorry at all. 'I didn't expect to find you in bed at this time.'

It's not quite eight. Still, not as bad as my mother-in-law.

'I wondered if you'd like to earn some extra money this week?' she asks.

Of course I would.

She sits in the armchair and I think, if only I was wearing a nightie I could sit up and talk. I can't even reach my tatty old dressing gown. She's sitting on it.

I drag the covers up and hold them carefully in place as I sit up. Ryan groans and turns over. He's still asleep or doing a fine job of pretending.

'It's Mr Hatchard,' she says. 'He's ready to be discharged next week, but there's no way he can handle those stairs on crutches.'

'Oh no,' I say. 'He so wanted to come back here. There must be a way.'

I feel honour bound to fight his corner.

'I have a solution,' Mrs Banerjee says, proudly. 'I've persuaded Albert to swap rooms with him. All we have to do is sort everything out. Just Mr Hatchard's stuff, of course. Albert's daughter will help him to move.'

Albert lives in the big sunny room with the bay window at the front of the house. It's a room I have lusted over, even though our little flat at the back of the house is more spacious, it's so dark in comparison.

'Albert's willing to give up that lovely room?' I say, enviously.

'Oh yes,' Mrs Banerjee says. 'The rent for the room upstairs is cheaper, so he's happy. Mr Hatchard is so pleased to be coming back here, and so he's happy to pay a bit extra.'

I see how pleased she's looking and I have a feeling she's charging 'a bit' more for both rooms. They'll never know. I will though. I hate this part of the job.

We need to sort through all Mr Hatchard's things, before Monday. If we pack everything into boxes and clean the room up ready for Albert to move in, Tomachevski will move the boxes down on Monday and help Mr Hatchard arrange his room when he gets back.

Tomachevski, *call me Tom*, is Mrs Banerjee's regular handyman. He's absolutely gorgeous and he knows it, and he flirts shamelessly with Mrs Banerjee. She might be sixty-something but she enjoys it. I wouldn't blame her, but he creeps me out.

I am doubtful. I'll lose all my weekend.

'I'll pay you twenty-five pounds,' she says.

Of course, I say yes. Ryan grunts. He's not asleep.

'I'll give you half an hour to get up and get some breakfast,' she says. 'Then we can get started.'

Ryan grumbles at me a bit but he feels the lure of the cash as strongly as I do. And he can have a lazy weekend.

Mrs Banerjee is back just as I'm eating my last bite of toast. I'm in my oldest jeans and pullover. I collect the cleaning gear from under the stairs and follow her up to Mr Hatchard's room. It's even more cold and unwelcoming now that it's been empty for so long.

Tomachevski has left a pile of cardboard boxes ready to be made up outside the door.

'We'll go through all his stuff first,' Mrs Banerjee says. 'There's not that much. Get it into the boxes and get them down to the storage cupboard and it can all be locked up down there until Albert's out of his room. His daughter's coming to move him tomorrow, so if we make a big push today we can have this room all ready for her.'

Ah. I was going to earn my wages in one very long and exhausting day. I suppose at least that would give me

Sunday to recover.

We have a quick look round the room.

'It doesn't look as if he has any kitchen stuff of his own,' Mrs Banerjee says. 'Just the basics that come with the flat. We can leave those for Albert, unless he wants to bring the ones he's used to. Just wash them and make sure none are cracked and chipped.'

That leaves the contents of the wardrobe and the chest of drawers.

I make up half a dozen boxes and we start on the wardrobe. There isn't much, but it is all well cared for. A couple of overcoats. Three suits. Several pairs of trousers and a blazer. Three pairs of black shoes, all beautifully polished. A row of white shirts. There's an old silk dressing gown hanging on a knob inside the wardrobe. Mr Hatchard had come down in the world.

As I fold everything carefully and placed it all in the boxes, Mrs Banerjee talks.

'I visited him in hospital a couple of times, to get all this agreed,' she says. 'It's as well I did. He had no other visitors at all, the nurses said. He must have no family. I asked him, but he was quite rude. He just didn't answer.'

I make a noncommittal noise. She doesn't really want me to carry my share of the conversation. An occasional nod is all that is needed to punctuate her soliloquy.

We pile the boxes of clothes by the door for Tom to deal with later.

Now, the chest of drawers.

Old fashioned shaving stuff, brush and everything, and his washbag and folded towels are neatly arranged in the top drawer.

'What has he been using in hospital?' I ask.

'Oh, I offered to collect some things for him but he refused. He was oddly insistent. The nurses bought him things and they even did some washing for him. He was quite a favourite with them.'

I pick up a couple of small boxes. Curious, I open the smaller one, feeling mildly guilty. Gold cufflinks in that one. The other, a larger flat box, contains a collection of medals. I don't know what they are, but I know they are special to him. He has so little. I am suddenly very sad for him.

Mrs Banerjee catches my eye.

'He probably bought them in a junk shop,' she says, mocking me.

I don't think so. Underneath there's some papers too. A certificate confirming an award. A letter in his name about long and honourable service. An old black and white photograph of him in uniform. He was a handsome man.

I consider speaking up for him – but what's the point? Mrs Banerjee has already told me her opinion of her tenants.

'Bedsits are fine for younger people like you,' she'd said. 'You're at the start of your lives. Everyone has to begin somewhere. But these are people who should have done well for themselves. There's a reason why they're here. Everyone finds their own level.'

The second drawer down is easy too. Pyjamas and underwear, all clean and neatly folded. That's another two boxes ready to go into temporary storage.

The bottom drawer. I pull it out and gasp.

It's crammed full of magazines. Top shelf magazines. Fiesta. Men Only. And more. They are all very well read.

Mrs Banerjee steps back.

'Dirty old man,' she almost spits.

'Rubber gloves,' she says. 'We should have been wearing them all along.'

She's afraid she might catch something. As if suddenly all his perfectly clean and laundered clothes had become retrospectively contaminated.

'We'll get these all into one big box and then Tomachevski can have a bonfire tomorrow.'

'Is that right?' I ask in a small voice. 'They belong to him.'

'This is disgusting,' she says, pausing between each word for emphasis. 'I don't want them in my property.' She gloves up and reaches gingerly into the drawer and takes out the top magazine. It falls open at a Readers' Wives spread. 'Look. The pages are stuck together. Ugh. No wonder he didn't want me to fetch his wash things.'

I'd tried. I should have tried harder maybe, but I needed the money. Rubber gloves on, I empty the contents of the bottom drawer into a big cardboard box.

Mrs Banerjee leaves me to it. She's seen everything there is to see. She has a dinner party that evening to prepare for and there isn't much left to do. Just fill the last box, and then give the room a good top-to-bottom clean.

She strips the bed – still in her rubber gloves – and takes the bedding with her. She'd deal with that in her washing machine at home.

At the bottom of the drawer, underneath the magazines, there's an even more secret stash of literature. A small collection of romantic Mills and Boon novels. Another wave of sadness for him washes over me. Mr Hatchard is an old man, all alone in the world. He's served his country. Like all of us, all he wants is some human connection, some warmth. Those sweet romances.

I imagine myself into the future. Sixty, seventy, maybe. Perhaps one day I'll be in the same position, old and alone, longing for some romance. For someone to want me. For someone to touch me. For someone to sleep next to me, body touching body.

I consider secretly keeping some of them for him. How would I choose? How would I give them to him without embarrassment – mine and his? I pile all his collection into the box for Tomachevski to burn.

The smoke from the fire brings a tear to my eye. Poor Mr Hatchard. How will he feel when he realises all his collection has gone? Angry? Embarrassed? I can't imagine him asking Mrs Banerjee where it is. Something else she will just get away with.

A couple of days later, there's a knock at the door of our flat, just ten minutes after Ryan has left for work.

I open the door and Mr Hatchard is standing there, leaning on crutches.

'You're home,' I say, stupidly stating the obvious. 'Good to see you looking so well.'

'I'm glad to be back,' he says. 'But there's one problem.'

Oh my God, I think. He's going to ask about his collection. I blush.

'I can't manage to tie my shoelaces,' he says, apologetically. 'I wonder if you could help?'

'Of course,' I say, and without thinking I sink to my knees.

33

ADEM AY
My Gilly & Me

A few weeks before my tenth birthday, I went to the toilet, as I really needed to pee.

Up until this point, my childhood had been one of security and comfort. The universe obeyed laws stipulated with unflinching confidence by my mother. With her as my guide, I felt the world a friendly, increasingly familiar place. Should something unexplained, even odd arise, it was to be celebrated and shared, not feared and kept secret. This all changed the moment I wandered into our cosy bathroom, pulled down my trousers, and pushed out yet another glorious arc of sun-kissed piss into the toilet bowl. For you see, the tip of my still prepubescent, still wholly un-mystical penis, was beginning to expand.

At first the lone bulge was quite modest, barely an irritant, a knobble on a pallid twig. But as the urine flowed with ever increasing abandon, alas, so too did the bulge begin to mushroom. A knobble became a pickled onion, a perfect sphere enwrapped in my foreskin, pulsing slightly, like a tramp curled in his sleeping bag on a frosty winter's night. I was alarmed. As the skin stretched, a barrage of neurons shot up my spine. Their simple message to mother brain: this hurts, a lot. I scanned my meagre collection of memories for a hint of what to do – perhaps a friend confiding something during playtime, an overheard adult conversation, even a thematic maths puzzle trying to link everyday experience with the abstract world of numbers. It was no good. There was no hint of what to do with expanding penises. And suddenly, mercifully, it was over. The urine was spent, the pain completely gone, my penis as plain and unassuming as when I'd pulled it from my trousers. It was as if the sorry saga had never happened at all.

I decided no one could know about such a bizarre occurrence. For the rest of the day, I thought of little else, and suddenly the world was a far more sinister place, where objects, any object really, could rebel and start expanding at random. The need to pee, when it inevitably came, hours later, was like a death knell to my childhood. For the next hour I contorted and twisted, squeezed and fidgeted, a frayed spirit fighting inner demons. But my bladder would not be silenced, and penis in hand, I moped to the same thigh-high toilet bowl, wishing on all that was good that proportions be respected, expansion be damned, that the problem would leave just as randomly as it had appeared.

The second time was worse. The torrent of pee burst forth like a split fire hydrant, so desperate was I to go. The pickled onion phase was left at the starting blocks. I was in ping-pong ball territory. The skin was so stretched it was actually approaching the pallor of a ping-pong ball. The pain was unbelievable. Worse still, the pressure was so acute the pee was shooting at an angle. The entire right side of the room was being doused in piss. I squealed and instinctively gripped with all my might the ballooning area, just beneath the head, squeezing it into submission. The relief was glorious. Yes the pee arc was interrupted, as if imaginary rocks were cutting into its stream, but urine was still leaving me, and with an iron grip on the vigilante section, acute pain and rampant expansion became as outmoded concepts as bike stabilisers and doggy-paddle.

With the patented "clamping down with both hands" method, I was able to pee quite happily. I honestly don't remember how long this quick fix lasted. It was certainly a day or two, but it could have been longer, say a week. One thing is certain; it wasn't long before it stopped working. My penis's need for expansion was just too great, and being a quiet, not particularly athletic child, the muscles in my arms and hands were no match for such arcane, primordial urges. It was when my grip slipped and I felt my foreskin might actually split that I decided a parent must become part of this deadly equation. My description of the events that christened every toilet break was met with one part bafflement for every two parts alarm in my mother. Perhaps suspecting an overactive imagination she demanded to be invited in on my next toilet break so she could see for herself what I meant by "so big it might pop".

The doctor explained, between giggles, that I suffered from Phimosis. I want you to understand – he was not laughing at my predicament. He was laughing at what I called my penis, a mispronunciation appropriated from my immigrant father, and never corrected by a mother who couldn't stand such a personal bastion of cuteness disappearing altogether. To now return to Phimosis – essentially my foreskin was not growing, though the rest of me was, and the sheath of skin increasingly resembled a very tight rubber band fused to my penis, or as I called it, my gilly. The solution was something quite routine, something successfully achieved hundreds of times every day. It was circumcision.

If the world turns out to be controlled by some divine force, it is obviously quite the fan of black comedy. Having quickly appropriated a bed in the local hospital with my patient name as Mr. Ay (I later found out the condition can lead to gangrene and amputation if not operated on), I was introduced to my young Chinese anaesthetist, Dr. Me. Dr. Me told Mr. Ay as he lay prostrate, flaccid penis there for all to see, that the normal local anaesthetic, given via injection, and prone to make the victim very nauseous, would not necessarily have to be given. I had luckily stumbled upon a trial period of another local anaesthetic, one already tested on hundreds of patients, and with no discernible side effects. Better yet, it was a cream, one to be gently applied to the penis a few minutes before the operation. Essentially, the horror of a vomit-inducing needle, plunged into my nether regions, had been snuffed out by the joy of gentle stroking. It was an easy choice to make.

The last thing I remember before the operation was having an oxygen mask put over me, and Dr. Me asking me to count, aloud, to ten. I decided I would count to eleven, if only to show off my boyish tenacity. The darkness consumed me around four.

I am not sure what actually happened when I came round as I really cannot remember. I was told I jumped up near-vertically and had to be held down by three nurses who then strapped me to the bed and gave me a shot of morphine. The pain was so raw, so overwhelming, I couldn't locate the source, barely really understood where I was. I couldn't even scream – my muscles were just contracting involuntarily, straining towards some internal singularity, as if I was swallowing myself up. My teeth chattered non-stop. Adhering to the great British tradition, I apologised profusely, though I'm not sure if I was understood. My mother was desperate, her eyes bulging with fear, dare I say it, like some twin reincarnation of my ping-pong ball penis. There was an argument about morphine – one nurse wanted me to have more, another said I was too young and they should wait. Time passed. It seemed forever. I felt like I was on fire, I couldn't see properly, someone kept slapping me to stop me passing out. To this day, when I think of agony, I think of waking up to that.

To take a moment to explain – the cream, the wondrous, brand-spanking-new local anaesthetic, was worthless. Ultimately it was little more than a white creamy placebo. The hundreds of glowing reports had come exclusively from children under two. Or in other words, babies. Babies whose pain receptors were still growing. Babies who cried and gurgled as it suited them. Babies incapable of giving feedback sophisticated enough for even the most quack of drug trials. I was a guinea pig, I took a chance, and I lost.

In a way, having a part of your penis sliced off with not even a crumb of a painkiller is a family tradition. My father would later tell me that in the Turkish village where he grew up, a man with a specially curved circumcising knife would travel the area, calling for fathers to bring their sons to the local tea shop. There they would be unceremoniously hacked apart on a wiped table, then sent off to buckle over and cry behind a tree or rock or some other rustic icon that surrounds such places. Perhaps fate will again play its hand. Perhaps my son will find his penis being diced open in some bizarre causal chain, one also involving random biological dysfunction and a disintegrating NHS. Whatever the future holds, I hope that I am the last of my kin to drown in such blinding woe. I hope that one day, one day soon, an Ay man will be buried in the ground after a long life, and his body will be beautifully, and absolutely, intact.

LIAM HOGAN
Better Babies

The night before Malcolm's first donation at the Harley Street sperm bank, he stuck his junk into work's X-ray machine and gave it a short blast.

Malcolm was not a doctor, or a dentist, or other healthcare professional with a rudimentary grasp of biology and medical processes. He certainly wasn't a radiologist. He was merely a design engineer at a welding company.

They used their X-ray machine to check the integrity of joints on high-spec jobs. Ones where a hairline fracture or incomplete weld could turn out to be very costly. It was not intended for irradiating testicles.

So Malcolm wasn't sure how long to leave them in for.

There was no one to ask. He was alone in the darkened factory under the railway arches, arches that were once the stomping ground of East End gangsters, the Krays included. Supposedly, he was working on the designs for a nozzle for a margarine manufacturer, to make up for the time he would lose during his mid-afternoon appointment at the IVF clinic the next day.

That was what he'd told his boss, without of course mentioning IVF, or the exact nature of his "medical reasons". His boss, after looking around the silenced, motionless factory floor and then up at the little pool of illumination of Malcolm's CAD workstation in the cramped upstairs office, had shrugged and thrown him the heavy set of keys.

"Don't forget to lock up," he shouted, his voice

habitually loud to cut through the cacophony of his chosen career, "or I'll be spot welding you to the rafters!"

Malcolm had laughed—politely—and then waited five minutes before embarking on phase two of his plan.

He almost gave up at the first obstacle, realising the buttons to operate the X-ray machine were a lot further than arm's reach from the blunt gun from which the X-rays emerged. Even if they'd been closer, he'd have to bend his body around the rigid lead apron that protected the machine's operator.

But he was, after all, an engineer, so it hadn't taken more than a moment or two to undo a few screws and drag the now free-range control panel to a stool just to the side of his position.

A little knowledge, they say, is a dangerous thing, and so it was with Malcolm. He had been told that X-rays cause damage to DNA, which can cause mutations.

Problem was, Malcolm was hooked on Marvel comics and X-Men films. Mutations, as far as he was concerned, were a good thing.

Once, while house-sitting for his brother and his newlywed wife, he'd discovered a book hidden beneath their bed: "The Better Baby Book". He'd been disappointed to find it was all about diet and the calculation of monthly cycles.

He figured there wouldn't be any real life superheroes, not until someone was prepared to be bitten by a radioactive spider, or to perform idealistic but dubious experiments on themselves in the name of science.

Such as X-raying their gonads.

Malcolm was prepared. Malcolm was going to do his bit. To his bits.

Sure, he wasn't stupid. He knew that doing this wouldn't give him superpowers. This was for the next generation. He also knew that not all mutations were good. But, he figured, with a little luck, at least one of the millions of tadpole sperm would weather the X-ray storm and emerge with some beneficial enhancement or another. And that plucky little sperm might be the one to make it to the egg in the clinic's petri dish. The odds weren't dissimilar to winning the lottery, perhaps, but people DID win it, so there was a small but finite chance he was about to do something wonderful. To kick-start a new stage in human evolution.

And that, surely, justified the effort.

Again, he didn't expect to sire someone who could fly, or shoot laser beams out of their eyes. He'd settle for something more modest. Someone who could dash the 100 metres faster than Usain Bolt. Who could cure cancer in their own body. Or... a genius, perhaps?

He studied the X-ray machine's controls. He considered dialling the intensity down to its lowest setting. That way, he could deliver a low dose for a long time. But would it be effective?

He feared not.

A high dose, for a very short time, was probably preferable, DNA disruption wise.

Ultimately, his experiment was predicated by the limitations of the X-ray machine. Its highest setting was capable of peering through inch thick steel, its shortest exposure was 25 milliseconds.

He checked he was in position, checked the cold strips of lead he'd stuck down his boxers were roughly in place, and the metal tube he'd inserted half his penis into wasn't encroaching on the target area. And then, stilling his breathing, he counted down, 3, 2, 1...

And stabbed the large green button.

He was pretty underwhelmed with the results. The slight tingle he might have felt could easily be dismissed as a figment of his imagination. Only the imaging system convinced him that the machine had in fact fired, that his meddling with the control panel hadn't in some way caused a fault. The image wasn't much of an image, there was no sign of anything organic, just the slightly off-centre steel tube, like some oversimplified Man Ray print.

He shrugged, thought about trying a second dose, before deciding that, as he'd signed up for ten donations (more possibly, depending on volume), he would lengthen the exposure each time. That would be the safest, most scientific approach.

He put the machine's console back together, closed down his workstation, and left, not forgetting to lock up.

* * *

In the brightness of early morning he stirred gingerly, feeling something wet and cold at his crotch. Lifting the sheet, he saw a no-longer frozen bag of peas. A flashback to waking in the middle of the night, uncomfortable, an itching, burning sensation. He lifted the mushy legumes.

A little red, a little sore looking. A little swollen, perhaps. Definitely swollen. But... not so bad. A pair of loose fitting trousers, today. Perhaps he'd go commando as well.

He was glad he did. Work was... difficult. He found it hard to focus, hard to sit still. Things felt awkward, down below. He was also glad to leave early for the clinic, truth

43

be told, fairly certain that he had done more damage than good to the margarine nozzle's intricate design with that half-day's inattentive efforts.

He stood for the short tube journey to Oxford Street, stood in the basement reception of the Harley Street clinic, ignoring the seats and the magazines and the potted plants. The short-haired receptionist smiled, recognising him from his previous form-filling visit.

Or perhaps the smile was her standard put your clients at ease smile. He wondered if the receptionists ever got embarrassed. Maybe they'd been working there too long for that, seen and heard everything.

She showed him to a door, one of many down a long thin corridor. "Here you go," she said, still smiling. "Take your time. Anything you need, just ask. I'm here to help."

How often, he thought, did what donors asked for merit a swift slap round the face? Or was she really offering what it sounded like she was offering? Surely not.

He smiled thinly in reply and closed the door firmly behind him.

The windowless room had a sofa, a wipe-clean armchair, and a discrete box-file for porn. Light streamed from the en suite. He pushed that door half closed, put down the small plastic pot next to an industrial-size roll of paper towels and slowly unzipped.

Angry red flashed back at him. As if he'd caught the sun in a peculiarly localised area. Which, in a way, he supposed he had. There was even a sharp dividing line where the steel tube had sat, and a geometric arrangement of equally sharp red lines from the gaps between the lead strips he'd inserted down his pants.

Thank God he'd done that. He'd have to come up with

a more efficient shielding technique for next time.

But the primary target: his balls... his balls seemed almost to glow, the skin stretched tight, the size, not of plums, but of small oranges, or large satsumas.

He winced and had a sudden wistful image of a family-sized pot of cooling yoghurt.

That would have to come later. He'd not bother returning to the factory. He'd take it easy, a cool—no, a *cold* bath perhaps, and something soothing from the chemists. For now, he had an important job to do.

Painful though that might prove.

But, if he didn't, then this would all have been for nothing, and he'd be denying some lucky recipient the results of his now supercharged sperm.

He opened the box of porn.

It was an odd assortment. He guessed it was there to cover all tastes. He quickly discarded the ones that reminded him of his mother and even more quickly those with naked men on the cover. Selecting from the remainder at random, he flicked one open, and gazed at the earthy charms of the girl-next-door figure.

Tenderly, he grasped the upper half of his member, the touch refreshingly cool.

Turning the pages, he tuned out the all-too-realistic images, let them instead inform his subconscious, while he imagined buxom superheroes peeling themselves from skin-tight costumes, the ruins of some apocalyptic battle in the background.

He was surprised, but not very, that when he lifted his mind's eye gaze from the gravity defying cannonball breasts, it wasn't Halle Berry as Cat Woman, or Rebecca Romijn as Mystique, or even Brigitte Nielsen as Red Sonja;

it was the cute elfin face of the receptionist that smiled and winked back.

Slowly, he coaxed a stiffening, careful not to tug too hard. He reached for the sample jar, unscrewed the lid, and then had to start all over again.

It took longer this time. As he cycled through the slightly tatty magazines his mind kept drifting from the task in hand and, whenever it did, he deflated faster than an undercooked soufflé. There were involuntary yelps whenever he pulled too hard, or too far down the shaft, the sudden flare of pain stopping him in his tracks, forcing him to readjust his grip onto the section of paler flesh further along before trying to ease back to the same point.

Finally though, he could sense the inevitable end. He quickened his pace, ignoring the twinges of pain from overstretched, tortured skin. Careful to keep going, he grabbed the pot with his other hand, closing his eyes for the blissful moment—

"Is everything okay in there?" came a voice through the door.

He gurgled in reply, wrist spasming, rhythm destroyed, the specimen pot dropped and rolling beneath the sofa as the door creaked open. The receptionist stuck her head in. "It's been 45 minutes and—OH MY GOD!"

It wasn't the two-tone, rapidly shrinking penis she was staring at. In the half-light, his grapefruit-sized balls were glowing, *actually* glowing. Not simply an angry, sun-scorched red, but throbbing like a Belisha beacon, in tune to his rapid heartbeat, his pubic hairs sticking out like antenna, a dark web of blood vessels crisscrossing the pulsating fire below.

He looked up into her shocked face, her widened eyes,

the perfect O-shaped mouth. Took in the way her arched body thrust her breasts forward, stretching her blouse. And then he lowered his gaze to his superpower-endowed, glistening, incandescent testicles, and... *came*.

ALEX CARRIGAN
How I Lost My Virginity in a Lobster Trap

NoahMacArthurShow
September 4, 2018

Ever been curious to know how (one of) your (presumably) favorite YouTube stars had his first sexual experience? Probably not, but Noah's gonna tell you anyways.

(Note: I was definitely 18 when this happened. Don't flag this video.)

Video Transcript:

(Noah is sitting in front of his computer in his bedroom. He is wearing a small sailor hat, a red neckerchief, and a pale blue t-shirt that reads: "I Got Crabs in Myrtle Beach.")

Noah: Hello. My name is Noah MacArthur, and today, I'm going to tell you all how I lost my virginity in a lobster trap. Now, I know what you're all thinking: Noah, you beautiful blond court jester with great cheekbones, why a lobster trap? Why not lose it in a cheap motel on your prom night? Or in the backseat of a Camaro during Pride? Why did you choose to give it up before you got legally married because premarital sex is a sin and doubly worse since you're marrying a guy?

Well, *Grampa*, we can't all have much say in when it happens. It's like when you find a movie where Adam Sandler is actually a decent actor in it: you just sit there and let it happen, and then you allow yourself to feel some joy in having experienced it because the odds are you will never experience it again.

But I guess I should explain how it happened. Okay, so, I was on the east coast for a family trip to Boston this summer. That's why I didn't produce anything in August. This is also a good reason to remind you to follow my Facebook page or follow me on Twitter @NoahMacArthur4Eva so you don't have to go up-in-arms when I have a slight video drought. Don't worry, if I'm gone for some time, it's so I can generate stories like this one.

(The URLs for his Facebook page and his Twitter appear on the bottom of the screen)

Now, back to the story.

We were going to go see all the Boston sights: the harbor, a Red Sox game, the alley Casey Affleck sleeps in, when one night, I was all by my lonesome. My mom and grandparents wanted to call it an early night, and I wanted to go out and enjoy Boston all on my own. I mean, I am perfectly legal now, so might as well.

So, I make my way to the waterside and I see this raging party on a dock nearby. I figure, "Why the fuck not?" and made my way there. So I get in, I'm dancing, I'm putting the fake ID I bought for $50 to good use, and then I met this guy named Jeremy. Now, he was pretty good looking. I'm talking dark black hair, well-toned body, aquiline jaw: the whole Italian-Bostonian fantasy.

So I make eyes at Jeremy from across the dock, we meet up, we chat for a bit, and then we decide to go for a walk. It's a beautiful night, I really don't have to be at my hotel any time soon – thanks to my mom for deciding I was old enough to have my own hotel room. So Jeremy and I are walking along the shore, and it's super beautiful. Like, I'm totally expecting fireworks to go off like I'm in a Nora Ephron film or something it's just that picturesque.

Anyways, we come up to this old shack and we decide to check it out. I mean, it's not technically trespassing if no one can prove you were ever there, so, again, why the fuck not?

So Jeremy and I go inside, we look at all the nets and hooks, and we also notice the lobster traps. I had never seen a real one before. Now, I'm from Arizona, it's rare to get lobster unless you still have mafia connections, to which my broke-ass family doesn't. Well, anymore. Not since One-Eyed Dickie became a part of the desert ecosystem. And Jeremy's the kind of guy who grew up on boats, which totally explains his gorgeous tan, but he also gave me a demonstration.

He found the largest trap there, and noticed that it looked completely hollowed out, unlike most traps, and invited me to climb in. Now, I'm not some chick who dies in the first half hour of a January-released horror movie: I know what sounds like a trap. Anyways, I tell Jeremy I won't climb in, so he figures out the implication. Yeah, he thought this Arizona boy hadn't been nearly threatened into a dark, cramped place before. Well he should have known that that man really convinced me he had candy in his van, so I've learned from the mistakes of my past.

Anyways, Jeremy realizes that he is being as creepy as fucking Jeffrey Dahmer, so he decides to be a good sport and climb in himself, trusting me to not be a creepy Jeffrey Dahmer motherfucker myself. See, we were building trust this night, it's something you should try with one-night stands. Once he's in, he bets that I can get in too. I figure: why not? It's not like he'd be easily able to shimmy out and lock me in. So, I get on the floor, make my way into the trap, and suddenly, I realize I'm lying face-to-face to Jeremy. As I do, he closes the door to the trap. Now the fucking *Silence of the Lambs* fears come back, but before I say anything, Jeremy kissed me.

Then I realized that this Red Sox player was up to bat with his Louisville Slugger at the ready, or whatever the fuck kind of baseball bats they use in Boston. I don't follow that shit. The butchest reference I've made so far in this video was Adam Sandler, and he once got out-machoed by an ambiguously European female walrus trainer in that one movie.

So yeah, suddenly, being crammed in a tight metal cage that's slowly turning my ass into a chessboard got us both

51

really turned on, so we just began to make out. Of course, that just made it awkward to drop trou, so we both had to work within the confines of the space. Jeremy managed to unbutton my pants, but he suggested I roll over.

"Roll over?" I asked.

"Yeah. How else am I going to fuck you?" he told me.

And I said, "How do you know I'm not a top?"

And he was like, "Back at the party you let out a high-pitched squeal when you realized the DJ was playing Ariana Grande."

So I was like, "Fair enough."

Now, once you're packed tight like Jimmy Dean sausages, it's hard to do anything with your sausage. But hey, I was on vacation and here was a hot New Englander who totally wanted to fuck me, so I was down. So I started to slowly roll onto my side, in between grunts of "sorry" and "oops" and "hold on". Anyways, I was finally with my backside facing Jeremy, and he got by briefs down.

And then…

(Noah closes his eyes and puts a hand over his chest.)

Oh my god…

(Noah opens his eyes.)

So yeah, we're crammed, and he's just going in-and-out, in-and-out. Of course, because it's a tight space, he can't really move that much. After a while, it doesn't even feel like he's fucking me and more like a big turd just can't decide if it wants to drop out of me or not.

So I'm like, "Hey, this isn't really working."

And he's like, "Yeah, this wasn't what I had in mind."

And I'm like, "You had something in mind when you brought a guy into a cage to fuck him?"

"Well, yeah. I was going to fuck the guy and we'd have a good time," he said.

"So what do we do now?" I asked.

Then Jeremy was like, "I know. Roll onto your stomach. I'll just lie on top of you and fuck you that way."

I'm like, "Alright, sure," and we both started to roll over. Now, I've already had my cherry popped and just wanted this guy to do whatever he could to get me off. I deserved that at least. Unfortunately, it was then that I realized how awful an idea this was.

See, my pecker was still out, and when we rolled over, it rubbed against the cage. It was cold and kind of rusty, and I immediately shouted, "Oh shit!" and Jeremy was like "what?" and I said "Dude, what if I cut my dick on this cage? Could I get tetanus? What do I do if I get tetanus on my dick?"

He's like, "I don't know. They have antibiotics for that right?"

And I'm just freaking out like, "I don't know! What if it turns green and falls off or something?"

So I'm there thinking I caught something that's like gangrene and leprosy combined, so now we're both freaking out, but I thankfully had an idea.

"Okay, shit, let me cover myself in the front."

I had to awkwardly move to pull the front of my brief up, at least still letting my ass hang out for Jeremy to plow. Once I gave him the go-ahead, he began to pound my ass.

Now, we at least had some room up top so I could really feel it, and oh man, was it awesome. I mean holy crap did he break through me like the fucking Kool-Aid Man through a wall. Now, this felt great... for about ten seconds.

See, Jeremy started getting really into it and that caused me to get forced down into the floor. As he fucked me hard, my face started pressing against the cage, making my face look like I took a nap on a waffle iron. Unfortunately, Jeremy was really into it, so I had my face pressed against the bars of a cage, my covered dick rubbing against my underwear, and this hot guy on top of me whose first thought about taking someone to a fishing shack was to entrap them and fuck them. Clearly, I made good choices this evening.

Thankfully, Jeremy finally came, and once he did, I asked him to get off me so we could get out. Lucky for me, he was spent enough that he didn't want to trap me in the cage, so I knew I'd live to see the next sunrise. So we climbed out, and after we fixed ourselves up, we kind of had no idea what to do next. I mean, I was uncomfortably pressed into a small space and had my ass hollowed out by some guy I just met that night and was sure I needed a tetanus shot I could only get after one awkward-as-hell conversation with my mom. What was a guy to do after having the most awkward sexual encounter imaginable?

Thus, I fucked Jeremy against the wall. Turns out he was versatile, so that was fine with me. I didn't come in the lobster trap, so he at least owed me that. After that, we thanked each other for the nice evening and went our separate ways.

So yeah, that's how I lost my V-card. Jeremy, if you're watching this and we happen to run into one another in Boston or Kingman, let's just fuck in a bed this time. That trap messed me up. I went to a Red Lobster with my mom and got a boner the second I saw the lobster tank. I had to fake a shellfish allergy to get out of that situation.

But anyways, I hope you felt enlightened by that story and know not to make the same mistakes I did. Thanks for watching. Don't forget to subscribe.

(Noah gets up from his seat and begins to walk off-screen.

However, he stops and sits back down.)

Noah: Oh, and Jeremy, I did get that tetanus shot, so I hope you at least got one after I hollowed you out. I'm sure the last thing you need is your butthole to look like a moldy doughnut.

(Noah gets up from his seat and walks off-screen.)

Noah: *(off-screen)* Okay, now they have to believe I can actually get laid. Not like anyone actually wants to fuck YouTube stars anyways.

End Video

GAYELENE CARBIS
Dicks

The only thing I like about men is their dicks. And what they can do for me. What they can do *to* me. Their mouths their hands their muscular bodies. Not just their dicks. The feel of them hard against you, pressing. The thrust of them. The taste. How their backs are broad and their smell is never sweet, never sickly or foul like the smell of some women's cunts. I like my own smell but I can't ever come at going down on a woman because of the smell of it. I like my own smell, but I just don't want to smell other women. Makes me think of my mother. Not that I want to think of my father, I don't think of my father when I think of any man and his dick, but you know what I mean.

The long firmness of them, the hardness, that thrusting that threatens to split you in two and how they turn you this way and that way and go for it with such intention, such absorption and focus, keep going and going for it until the climax, how they're so driven about it and know what they want and go after it and get it.

I know what I want but I'm too scared to say. They don't like it when you just want to fuck. They want you to admire them, like them, love them, listen to them, be their best friend, and want them for more than just one thing. And they're sentimental. Clingy. They talk about love a lot. They have this need of you, this desire to be close to you. They keep fucking it up with their fucking emotions. Their *feelings*. They can't just say, we had a good time. Let's leave it at that. They get too involved.

I'm always wanting them to leave. Okay, we've fucked, it's done, it's over. Get out. Don't hold me all night in your arms and tell me how lovely it is to wake up beside me in the morning.

What do you think of me? What are you thinking? They never stop asking. You just want to fuck, you're standing around waiting and waiting because you've got to get through all this *talk* that precedes it – he wants to talk about work, and his relationships with his clients and colleagues, his family, his friends, his feelings about everything and all you can think is: I wish this were over, and we'd just get down to it.

But you stand there and listen politely and say the right things and do the right things and hope the talk will soon come to an end. But it's never soon enough.

Don't get me wrong – there's more to men than their dicks. They're complex and complicated and talk with them can be stimulating and relaxing and even enjoyable. But when it comes down to it – the thing I really want from them is sex and I don't really want all the other stuff. It takes too much time, it's too much hard work.

But they want you to want it. Relationship. Commitment. Monogamy. Marriage. They don't want to think or know you might be like a man. The only-interested-in-one-thing scenario. Why not? What's wrong with it? Why shouldn't I have it and not have all the other stuff?

I shouldn't say the only thing I like about men is their dicks, I like much more than that. It's men who've inspired me, mattered to me, men that I've loved most. But as I became more conscious – thanks to ten years in therapy – I got over Men with a capital M. Those old loves, they're dead loves now. My father; my beloved brother; favourite

58

uncle; Mr Father-Figure – my English teacher; my first real relationship, the man I loved – I don't feel that old way about them, I don't see them the same way. Besides, with none of them, it was never about sex, except for the last one. And the sex was only incidental, I was in love with him for his mind. Oh, but the sex *was* wonderful. While it lasted. And before ten years of therapy, which taught me a few things.

It's always about sex. That's what fucks it up. All that Oedipal stuff, as they say. I read it in a book somewhere. It said - when you want to fuck your father and he wants to fuck you but you both go around pretending that you don't, and no one admits that's what Oedipal really means. And it's not only daughters and fathers, or sons and mothers - it's sons and fathers and daughters and mothers. That's what we all forget. You can never look at someone in the same way after some things. But I knew what it was. It's when you pretend it's all nice and you're all nice and you never have those nasty difficult feelings. And all along you're enmeshed. Some families are like that, they really do fuck you up. My father fucked me up, I fucked up my brother (and he's never forgiven me), Mr Father-Figure fucked me over, and my first real relationship was fucked: that's a lot of fucking.

I should say, the main thing I like about them or the thing I like *most* about them. Yes, that's more specific.

I don't even really know if that's true, that I only like their dicks. By which I really mean, their bodies. It's just easier to deal with a dick than a mind or a heart or a... a *man*.

CHRISTINA LOVIN
Two Doves

"I tried real hard to forget what happened back then, Reverend. Even being one all growed-up woman didn't let me put it out of my mind. You know well as anybody how many times I prayed to God Almighty that He take those old hurtful thoughts from my mind and ease my fretful heart so as I can just get on with my life and my children and the Lord's work. But it done stuck in my craw, you know? Now this…"

Charlene stops and looks at me. The red rims of her eyes seem to blaze around the deep gray of the irises, making them appear almost blue in contrast. Her gaze is quietly defiant but the gaunt face seems tired, almost resigned, as she lowers her thin eyelids. Tears puddle in the creases at the sides of her eyes, then fall on either side of the drawn face, old beyond its thirty-two years. If eyes are the windows to the soul then Charlene's soul is already feeling the flames of Hell, fiery red and wounded as they are.

She twists the frayed rectangle of what had once been a pale flannel fabric, but is now nothing but a rag—a dismal, colorless gray. The dishes she had been washing when I knocked on the farmhouse door have slipped beneath the gray water, viscous with cold grease clotted together with the hard soap the women around here use to clean everything from clothes to skin. It is Thursday. I know that the dishwater is only fresh on Monday; that a bit of hot water is added each day until Saturday when the sink is scrubbed with lye and sand to be clean for the Sabbath. It is

60

the way of the women here. It is my way now.

The light inside the kitchen is low as I have become accustomed to in this place of impoverished and penitent people. I am their shepherd, their pastor, their link with God. *True religion is this: to visit the sick and the widowed.* That saying is in the New Testament somewhere. Beyond the Gospels, the Holy Bible becomes blasphemous babble to God's true flock. Jesus was the end of the line for God, and even he was just a mere reflection of what the Almighty had intended. We know this in these hills. We have been chosen to live the old ways, older than Christianity, more right and real. Jesus himself said, *I have not come to destroy the Law, but fulfill it.* He knew. And we know. That is why I am here with Charlene: to do what needs to be done—to heal her and make her whole in spirit. Charlene shudders as if knowing my thoughts or reading my mind. She may be a seer, but would never say. We would have to kill her if she was.

"Reverend, ain't memory strange? The past is long gone. All the bad things that ever happened to a soul are over and done with, seems. Sort of dead and all, cold and stiff as a corpse. But I seen them little Clayton boys out on the hard road sometimes, pushing pointy sticks clear into the guts of them dead, bloat-bellied carcasses stretched out in the gravel beside. They know them yellow teeth and black claws can't do no harm, but they jump and squeal at the first riffle of a breeze or wriggle of a maggot. They think them things is come back to life. Bad memories are like that, huh? There's some scary-hot place at the back of your brain that keeps waiting for the first sign of life. Them that's forgotten are the lucky ones. Them and the dead."

Kerosene fumes from an ancient glass lamp foul the

air, but the kitchen is shadowy just the same. A wall of cupboards rises to the low ceiling and a deep counter top extends back into almost total darkness below them. The counter is cluttered, but the muted light reveals some of what is scattered and piled there: a dented aluminum pan, the blackened copper of a teakettle—green around the lid where moisture has corroded it—and a stack of folded rags much like the one Charlene is wrapping and unwrapping from her left hand. I lean back in the bow-backed kitchen chair. The spindles dig into the flesh of my back, making the scars itch satisfactorily. I thank the Lord each time I remember the long striations that are welted on my skin, a reminder of my own sin. My own salvation.

The grimy glass of the window looks out over the dooryard of the small leaning house. Charlene's children were playing there when I walked up to the home where she and her late husband Dell Westfall lived together until the buggy he was driving on his egg route was struck by a car a year ago. Perhaps the children know why I am here. They sit in a row on the wooden fence like three crows on a wire, their dark hair and woolen garments stark against the white-gold corn stubble that rises behind them across the rutted dirt road.

Ammery, the oldest at thirteen, stares evenly toward the house. I shift a bit in my chair as I feel the weight of her gaze, knowing that she most likely can't really see me, just sense me sitting here. She is like her mother in many ways: dark, chestnut-colored hair, the same high bosom and long legs. Perhaps she has some extra sense like her mother. Theo and Franklin, the nine-year-old twins, glance nervously up the road, then back at the house as if expecting help to arrive. The job of gathering, candling, and delivering eggs to the store at Five Corners three miles away fell to them when their father died. A family still has to eat, even if the man of the house is gone. Ammery was hired as a maid's helper—washing dishes, sweeping, making beds—at the home of one of the new strangers to the area. The outside world has been finding the quiet and charm of this place over the past few years—both a balm and a bane to the local parishioners.

Charlene lifts her gaze from her strong, callused fingers. The hands are laced together now, as if in supplication—the short, ragged nails white at the ends as the fingertips push into the knuckles of the other hand. I see the release of one finger after the other as the two palms separate, then are splayed flat on the oilcloth spread over the rickety wooden table. She slowly moves her eyes from where the fingers of her right hand are caressing the crease where a wedding ring might have rested had our people believed in wearing any jewelry. Her long hair, once shiny like her daughter's, now like old straw, drab with poor nutrition and outright weariness, moves slightly off her shoulder, the uneven ends dropping below her bent elbow. Her profile is soft against the murky light coming in through the small windows, but I know her chin to be firm, her nose almost regal. She looks wearily out at the three children for what seems several minutes. Ammery's returning stare is constant and dark. Charlene turns to me again, her voice husky with what might be pain. She breathes in and out, gathering courage. Or is it some silent rage?

"This weren't nothing new, you know. Ammie reminds me of myself at thirteen—all white skin and glossy hair. But she got those blue, blue eyes what don't even look real, but more like them painted-on eyes of that dime store baby doll I had before Ma and Pa joined the flock. Ammie ain't never had a doll. Abomination, graven image, we been told now. My children never had no toy, no presents at all, not on they own age days nor even Jesus's. That's all right. They good kids, even so. Maybe better, if the Book can be believed. I was a good girl, too. Pretty somewhat. Leastwise people done said that before my hair gone all dingy and my body all slumped down. But that don't make no difference to him, anyhow. He just like the young ones, you know? The ones who are most about ripe, but too scared to talk. Like me back then. Like the others. Like Ammie."

The tears have dried on her strong face. Grim resignation and something even harder have replaced them. I can see it in her narrowed eyes and the clenched jaw, the tense fingers as the two hands grasp one another. "I was just a slip of a girl when Jimmy and Erlene first had me for a night-over. First and last time. But too late just the same. This pains me to speak of, Reverend, but I leave it to you to tell the flock when the time is right. Or let me testify at prayer service after today."

She is eyeing me evenly now. I nod, but I am not sure with what I am agreeing. She continues: "Jimmy and me was in the barn that night, after the duskdown milking. The light was low like it is in this here kitchen. I was petting a new baby calf when Jimmy crept up on me all quiet-like from the back, putting his big old beefy arms around me. It was sort of like my mama would do when she came up on me staring out the window all day-dreamy sometimes. I wasn't scared, and it felt kinda good, but it didn't feel like it was the right thing, so I scrunched down to get away from him. But he held me fast. Tighter than you hold a baby boar you cutting. I couldn't hardly get no air. He spoke his old hot, rotty-teeth breath right on my neck, with his voice all raspy like he been running. 'You done growed into a mighty big girl now,' he say to me. I remember it perfect. Won't never forget it. I was just barely past my number thirteen day. Not started flowing like a woman yet. My biscuit never been buttered, like mama say. I weren't no big girl at all, just a scared young'un. Scared of him touching his tobaccy-stained fingers on my nippies what was just budding. More scared of how it felt down to my privates when he lift up my skirt and touch me down there. Then he pushed me down and started grunting and slobbering over me like some old boar over a sow at mating time. I start hating him then, and I never stopped, nor stepped foot in his house nor barn, nor got close to him ever again. 'Til now. No matter what the Book of Laws say. My mama kind of knew I think, but I would never tell her straight out. I never told nobody none of this until this here minute, Reverend."

She looks directly at me, her eyes cold and her gaze level. She nods slightly as if agreeing with herself somehow, then continues. "It weren't for me, you know. If it hadn't been for Ammie, I would have let the Lord mete out His own punishment. *Vengeance is mine, I will repay, thus sayeth the Lord.* I know that, Reverend. I been a God-fearing member of the flock most of my life. I know how many steps on the Sabbath from the house to the outhouse. I know it's too far for a member of the flock to walk, so I piss in the pot behind the door there 'til Monday. I never cut my hair, not mark my body, nor mix wool and linen. I won't never slander my neighbor, not even when Jimmy got poor Nonie Jepson with child and she die from the Butcher up to the big town. I never stole, not even when my Dell got himself killed and we got nothing here to eat for nigh onto a week, except the eggs we need to sell to buy milk and grain. I never cheat nor lie, even to save myself. I read the Book of Laws cover to cover every year like we been taught, and never peek into the parts after the Gospels. I am a good woman, Reverend. But, damn Jimmy and me both to hell—he touched my baby!"

Charlene slumps back into her chair, the small rounded shoulders shaking with sobs that rock the table as she leans against it. The dingy gray flannel gives off a sour stench as she lifts it to her face, dabbing at her eyes. She looks back out to where Ammery sits hunched on the fence still resolutely facing the house, her knees drawn up under her elbows, her face indistinguishable in the low light of dusk. Charlene looks directly at me then rises abruptly to her feet, knocking the shaky chair over on its side. Ignoring the chair, and stepping around the splayed legs, she walks the few steps to the shadowed counter below the cupboard shelves. Her right hand closes around one of the rags folded there, her left reaches into the blackness at the back of the counter. She turns around with what looks to be one of those olivewood Bible boxes sold by traveling book salesmen around these parts years ago. The box she gently lays on the dingy red oilcloth as she walks past me toward the other end of the kitchen.

A gigantic black cookstove is set up on a bed of fieldstones in the small, dark kitchen. The stove is cold and the room has fallen to a chill. The corn stubble across the road appears almost ghostly now as the warm light leaves it and the sun slips behind the hills to the west. I can see Ammery's outline against the harvested field—a black smudge on old, yellowed paper. The light from the kerosene lamp fails to reach the other end of the kitchen. I turn in my chair, but can barely make out what Charlene is doing, although I hear her sigh heavily. It seems that the rectangle of drab flannel cloth is spread out on the surface of the stove, but even straining my eyes I can't be sure. Charlene crooks a finger into the hole of one of the back burners of the stove, lifting it enough to snake her hand down the gaping hole. She withdraws something black and charred, placing it carefully on the cloth. The heavy burner cover clunks back into place when she releases it. She then picks up the lid to the reservoir of the stove and reaches inside. I hear the slush of water and what must be ice—a luxury this time of year—as she gropes around in the darkness. I can see her pull a slightly larger, pale object out of the reservoir and place it beside the black and charred object. The four corners of the cloth are drawn together and secured by two knots. She lifts the bundle from the stove, and walks across the kitchen into the dull glow of the kerosene-lit table, then quietly lays the bundle in front of me. She points at it, then speaks almost matter-of-factly.

"I expect the sheriff is looking for these. I heard tell at Five Corners that they found Jimmy out there in the ruins of his barn. I knowed it was wrong, Reverend, but I couldn't abide what he did to my Ammie and the Book of Laws told it was right to do. That's why I took these. Like it says in Leviticus. You know, the part about the two doves? One for a sin offering, one for a burnt offering to make an unclean man whole? I done this for me and Ammie, and I guess for Jimmy too, seeings he was the one who needed the healing most."

Charlene bends down and peers into the soft darkness outside the window. She turns toward me with her back to the window almost as if blocking it from my view or blocking the view from the outside. With a motion of her hand, she indicates that I should open the lumpy gray bundle that lies before me. I already know what is wrapped inside. It was I who found the body, not the sheriff. The charred bones of what had been Jimmy Belcher were still hot when I got to his smoking barn, a low pile of burnt boards and ash. I smelled the smoke as I rose for morning prayer just before the sun came up.

The bones were slumped into a pile next to where the barn door had burned and fallen in. At first I thought someone had locked Jimmy in the barn before setting it on fire, but then I noticed the arm bones. The bones of the forearm were splayed away from one another due to the intense heat. This was only possible because they had been shortened. Blunted. Chopped above where the wrist should have been. Jimmy had not been able to turn the simple wooden latch to escape, or perhaps he had fainted from loss of blood before the flames had engulfed him, a more merciful assessment. I prayed over his remains, asking forgiveness for Jimmy and his rumored perversions. Although I knew that the Book of Laws said his soul was lost, I pleaded for a blessing, for grace, as I scooped the bones from where they lay and carried them to the cistern. Somehow I knew then he would get it—grace, or some sort of redemption. Looking now at the bundle in front of me, I am sure of it.

My fingers are clumsy as I untie the knots of the thin but coarse fabric. The acrid smell of burned flesh flies up my nose as the cloth falls open. The thin light from the kerosene lamp burns low, but is enough to see the gruesome objects lying there. The charred fingers of one hand curl as if grasping for something. Hope, maybe? Salvation? The other is livid but almost pearly in the horror it holds—the raw flesh at the wrist is colorless, even the veins that extend beyond the edges have faded in the icy water. The fingers are stiff, but straight. A narrow gold band still wraps the ring finger, in some sort of macabre irony. I study the strange relics for a moment, then look up at Charlene. She stares intently into the wavering flame of the kerosene lamp. I can see the anger burning in her eyes, banked and hot.

"Reverend, I done that for Jimmy. Like the turtledoves—one for the sin offering, one for the burnt offering. I done it all the right way, like the Book of Laws say. I done that for him. That was for Jimmy. *This* is for me and Ammie."

I had forgotten the olivewood Bible box, its smooth varnished surface glowing in the lamplight. Charlene moves forward to the table and bends over it, turning back the lid of the box to reveal a black-bound Book of Laws. I nod at Charlene, but I am unsure what significance the Book has to her and Ammery, at least where Jimmy was concerned. She reaches down to the box and lifts the dark volume from its vault. I can see there is something else resting at the far end of the box: a cylindrical bundle a little thicker, but shorter than the fat homemade cigars smoked by men around these hills. The smell comes to me then. It is the smell of animals left dead along the highway, the stink of rotting flesh. The stench of vengeance.

Charlene steps to the wooden door and opens it, loose upon its hinges. A chill breeze sweeps around the kitchen, taking the rank odor with it. She takes a few steps out onto the porch and looks intently into the deepening evening. A few more steps, and she disappears into the darkness. I hear the low tones of her voice mingling with Ammery's higher voice as they speak quietly out near the fence. Then there is silence, except for the easy scuff of Charlene's feet on the packed dirt of the dooryard, and the soft sounds of the twin's voices and Ammery's quiet, indistinguishable answers growing distant. The mother steps back into the light that rings the square table. Leaning her weight on both her hands against the slick red oilcloth, her eyes looking directly into mine, she speaks softly.

"I done sent them down the road to my Uncle Josiah's place. They be all right there for the night, I reckon. He see to their welfare for a day or two if I can't take care of them. But Ammie's a big girl now, anyway. You know she been working at them new people's house? She's growing to be almost a woman I figure." She pauses, her eyes clenched, weary. Sighs. "I expect we should be reading some scripture now shouldn't we, Reverend?" She looks up to me for assent before picking up the Book of Laws from where it rests in the pool of blood red light. The pages open easily. They have been read and reread so many times before. The thin paper rustles lightly as she leafs through a few pages, then trails her finger down a column of scripture on a page near the front of the book. She clears her throat, then speaks softly, the sweetness of her husky voice in contrast to the dread the words elicit in me. "Deuteronomy twenty-five, eleven and twelve: *If there be a struggle and the woman reach out and seize the man's private parts who is not her husband, then you shall cut off her hand; you shall not show pity.* Thus says the Book of the Law. Thus says the Lord. Amen."

"Amen," I echo, then rise and follow the silent woman out the door, across the porch, and down onto the packed earth of the dooryard. The field of corn stubble gleams pale in the dusk of impending night. The barn looms black ahead.

THADDEUS RUTKOWSKI
Slip of a Knife

My penis gets cut off in an accident. But I don't know what kind of accident it is. Am I chopping vegetables and do I miss? Do I miss the carrot or celery stick, miss the cutting board entirely and sever the stick in my pants? Does the momentum of my arm carry the blade all the way past the counter and through the stalk of my dingus?

Or is it some other kind of accident? A sex-game accident? That would be more likely. It would be easier to lose your penis in a sex game than in salad preparation. Maybe my partner and I are engaging in knife play. Or tomahawk play. The tomahawk would be more suited than a knife to my identity as a person of color. In the guise of a native American, I will wield the tomahawk, and maybe it will be my turn first. And since I cannot go for a penis— since my sex partner has none—I will go for a breast. But I won't really cut it off—that would be wrong. I'll just pretend to cut it off—that is hot.

When it is my partner's turn, she can't go for the breast—since I have none—so she'll go for the penis. But maybe the feathered headdress falls over her eyes and her hand slips and actually chops off the pecker.

Luckily, I'll still have my testicular basket. This is not a story about (dare I say it?) castration. I am no *castrato*. My voice is still low, which helps when I am mistaken for a woman. I can say, "Did you call me ma'am?" or "Are you talking to me?" in my deepest voice when a counterman or clerk addresses me as a woman. And the server might say,

"Oh, sorry, I saw you out of the corner of my eye" or "I'm talking to you *now*." But I'll be ticked off anyway, because what is it that makes people see my gender as female? Is it my stature? Or is it my hair? Probably both: my short stature and my puffy hair.

I just don't have a schlong anymore. I don't have a sausage that is long. That's probably not what schlong means, however. It doesn't mean "sausage that is long". It probably just means "trouser snake". I don't have a one of those, either. When I open my pants, no snake strikes. The good thing is, I can't catch my trouser snake in my zipper by mistake. I won't have to dance around swearing "Sheesh and *Scheisse*, I've pinched my *Schwanz*!" I won't have to do the dance of the damaged dingus. I won't have to look for a pair of pliers to free my pinched pecker. The pliers can stay where they are in the toolbox, safe from the hands of a fucknut like me.

EDWARD APELDOORN
The Camera-Shy Cock

"Want to have sex on cam for a hundred bucks an hour?"

I answered 'yes' after the first four words and the show was scheduled for that evening. We had never done anything like that before.

After years of putting up with asshole bosses and horrible hours, my wife had recently quit her job to try her hand at online sex work. She became a webcam model, a cam girl, one of those foxy ladies in the pop-ups that are eagerly waiting for you to watch them dance, strip, and masturbate while they smile at your pathetic jokes. The money was good, really good, and three days into her new career, I quit my job, too.

And so it was that I found myself the unemployed trophy husband to a porn actress, setting up lights, washing lingerie, and whistling while I washed various sex-toys in the kitchen sink. Not a bad gig, all things considered.

But the thing about online sex work, it's a circus, an infinite maze of pornographic subcategories, fetishes, perversions, and desires that few people would ever voice in real life. Some men want to watch models fuck mechanized dildos, or get nude in public, or squat over the edge of the bathtub and piss. Some men want to buy women's underwear. They want panties which are brand new, or old and tattered and skid-marked, or which have been shoved up a vagina for twenty-four hours (along with video proof of the act). There are cam girls who specialize in humiliating men for their tiny penises and others who congratulate them for their massive, meaty cocks. There are cam girls who meet up in pairs or in groups to strap on strap-ons and pound each other through the night. And then there are cam girls who fuck their boyfriends on live video.

My wife was still trying to find her niche in the industry, and when one of her new fans asked if she was willing to have sex with her husband while he watched, she said she'd talk to me and let him know.

Of course, I said yes. Why wouldn't I?

As the hour drew near, I became feverish with excitement. My dick had been twitching excitedly in my pants the whole afternoon.

While my wife did her make-up and put on a strapless dress and nothing else, I set up lights in the living room. I opened the laptop, secured the webcam, and loaded up the site. The preview video feed showed me sitting there on the couch, grinning wildly.

"Right," said my wife, entering the room. "You ready?"

I was more than ready. I was eager. My heart thundered in my chest. In my pants, I already had an erection like the Eiffel Tower (specifically one of those six-inch replicas you can buy in any Parisian gift shop, but still). My wife reached around me to the laptop. She typed a message, waited a moment, and a new window popped up.

"Oh hey!" greeted a voice from the computer. "How you guys doing? I'm Zachary."

I stared, dumbfounded, at the round face that now filled up half the screen. Somehow, I hadn't considered this aspect of the work. It wasn't just sex and cash. We would be performing, for a person, a person who would be sitting there watching us. And we could watch him.

My wife answered him with her biggest, brightest smile and a little wave. After a moment, I managed a nod. It's not that there was anything wrong with the face on the screen (I have no doubt Zachary is a pleasant and amiable young man), it's just that I'd never been turned on by the image of a baby-faced, balding man in his early twenties with a strap of weak beard under his chin, wearing a t-shirt featuring an anime heroine. He blinked happily out of the screen like a living, breathing cliché.

"So," he said, "shall we get started?"

"*We?*" I mumbled, but already my wife was adjusting the camera.

On the screen, Zachary reached out of frame and grabbed a Mountain Dew. He smiled as he drank, leaned back in his chair, waiting patiently.

I felt my dick through my jeans. Semi-hard now. Could be worse.

My wife started to strip. She took her time. She spun, made eyes at me, teased. She flashed glimpses of her bare ass beneath the dress, tweaked her nipples through the fabric, played with her hair.

It helped. I forgot about the face on the screen, about the webcam, about the money. The next thing I knew my clothes were off, my cock was hard in my hand, and my wife stood naked before me.

"Very nice!" declared Zachary. "Now, why don't we start with some oral. Suck his dick."

My wife giggled. It wasn't her real laugh. It was the 'oh my god you're so funny!' laugh she had developed for cam. Zachary seemed to like it. I was the one about to get the blowjob, but he was the one beaming like a kid on Christmas morning. That's how it worked, I had to remind myself. This wasn't about us, it was about him. His viewing pleasure. His fantasy. And frankly, his orgasm.

I pushed this final image out of my head and tried to relax as my wife knelt and put me in her mouth. She began to bob up and down, moaning slightly, her back arched to push out her breasts. I glanced at the laptop. In our preview window, her body looked fantastic. Mine looked like melted candle wax.

Sitting up, I twisted to one side and held my head up to avoid making a double chin. It was harder than I expected. My wife had explained how making porn is never about pleasure or comfort or natural positions. It's all about the angles, about light and shadow, about the placement of the camera. Nothing else mattered.

"Now have him go down on you!" commanded Zachary, not unkindly.

My wife stood up, wiping her lips and grinning at me while making sure the real target of the smile was the webcam. She stretched out on the couch, lifting one leg and letting the other drape over the side. I crawled up between her thighs and bent to kiss her vulva, but her hands seized my shoulders and shifted them, ever so slightly, so that the camera would have a better view.

I tongued her clit and fingered her for a few minutes, trying to focus on her moaning and not the heavy breathing issuing from the laptop speakers.

Then our patron announced that he wanted us to fuck. I was harder than ever and climbed on top without delay.

"Hmm. No. This isn't right," said Zachary. I paused, my dick halfway into my wife and twitching, and waited for him to complete his thought. "In the pussy, I guess," he finally said, "but doggy style."

We changed position, my wife leaning forward with her elbows on the arm of the couch, her back arched, and her round ass in my face. I straightened up on my knees and placed a hand on either side of her thighs, but noticing the video feed, moved one hand onto her back instead, giving Zachary a better view.

"Yeah, yeah, yeah," he said from the laptop, suppressing a Mountain Dew belch with the back of his hand. "Put it inside her. Fuck her."

I grabbed my dick and tilted it downward with an effort. My erections tend to aim for the noon sun, so slipping inside a waiting vagina perpendicular to my body wasn't easy, nor was it enjoyable. The base of my penis felt pinched and over-extended, like this whole thing was some perverse physical therapy exercise.

My wife was still wet, and as I began to hump her, she matched my rhythm with backward gyrations of her own. I leaned in, breathing hard, and began to fuck her in earnest. Her asscheeks bounced against my thighs, warm and slick with sweat.

I happened to glance at the screen. Zachary's face was rigid and his body shaking wildly as his hands busied themselves, thankfully, off camera. My gaze moved across the screen to our preview window. I exhaled, squinting at the image. I barely recognised the man on the screen with his dick in my wife.

I was about to turn thirty, and my torso had almost finished its transformation from toned teenage flatness to squishy dad bod. Conical manboobs were sprouting. My belly was beginning to take on the sort of look that, had I been a woman, might have elicited some awkward 'Ooh! When's the due date?' interactions.

The flab. The double chin. The ripples washing over my pillowy love handles. I wondered where the years had gone. I contemplated the inevitable drag of time, the tick-tocking of clocks, and the skeletal finger of Death beckoning me to the End.

"What...the fuck...are you...doing?" my wife hissed through clenched teeth.

She had turned her head and was staring up at me with a manic grin plastered on her face. I looked down. My dick had slipped free from her vagina and stood propped between her asscheeks. I had stopped humping.

Clearing my throat, I gave myself a few seconds of vigorous tugging to stiffen things up again, then pushed back inside her.

The moment passed. Zachary didn't seem to mind the pause. His off-screen stroking hadn't slowed down.

He let us do what we wanted for a while, then, and my wife and I happily readjusted to lie on the couch, me on top with her legs wrapped around my lower back. I fucked her slowly, in and out, while kissing her nipples. She wrapped one arm around my neck and used her other hand to pleasure her clit.

Eventually, she whimpered contently and stretched her neck to give my ear a little bite and whisper a message.

"Twenty-five minutes. Almost done."

Zachary had paid for half an hour. He must have noticed the timing, too, for he now clapped his hands and announced, "Okay! Time for the big finale. I would like to see... Hmm..."

My wife disentangled her legs from around me and we both turned to watch the screen. Zachary sat back for a minute, running his fingers through his neckbeard, then his eyes lit up. He leaned forward and spoke into his computer microphone, enunciating each word.

"Reverse. Cowgirl. Anal."

"Reverse cowgirl anal?" I repeated.

"Yeah. You guys know it?"

I shrugged. I certainly knew *of it*. I mean, I understood the concept of a person turning around and squatting over a man in order to shove his rigid dick up their anus, but that wasn't the type of activity I had ever seriously considered being a part of, in either position.

My wife darted off cam for a minute, leaving me and Zachary alone. We exchanged tight-lipped smiles that didn't reach our eyes. He finished his Mountain Dew. I picked a piece of couch lint off my balls. Finally, my wife returned, a bottle of lube in hand. She pushed me back to lay flat on the couch, then lubed up her fingers and made a show for the camera of preparing her asshole.

I gave my dick a little flick.

My wife set aside the lube and climbed onto the couch. I swallowed nervously, eyes swiveling from her ass as it came nearer, to the baby-faced man so close to his camera that his breath fogged the image, to our own webcam, gazing unblinkingly like a hungry, judgemental eye. My vision started to blur. My heart raced. The room around me seemed to fade, to tilt, to spin. On the screen, Zachary licked his lips.

And as my wife's wettened asshole pressed against the tip of my cock, something truly magical occurred.

My erection vanished.

It seemed to happen almost instantly. One moment I was uncomfortably stiff, the next, my wang lay wrinkled and shrunken across my leg. I froze, an expression of deepest shame and grief on my face, which had gone bright red. All the blood that had been in my penis must have made its way to my cheeks instead.

My wife paused in her squatting descent. She wriggled her bottom experimentally, but all that happened was that her asscheeks squished my penis flat against my balls.

She turned, slowly, and looked at me imploringly. I shook my head, my eyes telling the story my lips could not: *Yeah, this isn't going to happen right now.*

She sighed. It was her true sigh, not some made-for-cam sound.

"So, Zachary," she said. "Do you mind if we take a three-minute break? We have to get... things... rebooted."

Zachary exhaled noisily. He nodded. He understood. A moment later, his video feed disappeared.

My wife's face and body snapped back to reality. Her shoulders slouched. Her playful smile stretched flat.

"What's up with your boner?" she asked.

"I don't know! It's just not working."

"Get it working."

"Oh, okay! But seriously? Reverse cowgirl anal? Is that a thing people do?"

"It's what he's paying for."

I groaned, feeling about three inches small, which incidentally, I now was.

She took my face in her hands. "Sweetheart. I love you very much. But I need you to get your dick hard so I can put it in my butt for five minutes. Then we can shake hands and be done with this. Forever, obviously."

I took a deep breath. She was right. This line of work wasn't for me or my otherwise-dependable penis. Five minutes. I just needed to stay hard for five minutes.

We looked down at my sleepy cock, sealed to my balls with sweat. I picked it up, gave its flaccid shaft a pathetic little stroke. Then another. My wife cleared her throat and sat up. She rubbed her boobs suggestively and flashed me a momentary cam smile. My dick warmed in my hand and began to stiffen.

"You got this?" she asked.

"Sure," I said, unsurely.

She turned back to the laptop.

Zachary returned. He had started on another Mountain Dew but set the bottle aside when my wife assured him that all was well with the world once more. He began to stroke again. I was still stroking, too. Our eyes met through the screen, only briefly. Not briefly enough.

My wife adjusted the camera one last time. I lay back on the couch, she positioned herself above me, then...

We fucked. I was hard enough, barely, to squeeze into her ass and stay there. The angle bent and prodded my dick as she bounced, and the lukewarm lube felt slimy and unnatural. I gave up trying to look thin or sexy on the screen and embraced the melted candle wax vibe. All of my attention, my concentration, my mental and physical energy was focused on that boner. I willed my penis to stay hard, even as it cried out for freedom and flaccidity.

Above me, my wife moaned in ecstasy as she approached a suspiciously sudden orgasm.

On the screen, Zachary was flushed and jerking violently. If he had a seizure at that very moment, there would have been no way of knowing.

My wife held her breath. Her body tensed up, her asshole squeezing like a vice on my dick, then her mouth stretched wide as she released a joyous outcry.

Zachary went, "*Uh-gug-gug-gug-gug-gug-gug,*" and fell off his chair.

Feeling that I should probably be acting out orgasmic bliss myself, I gave her asscheek a little pat and said, "Mm. Oh yes. My my." My dick was already going soft again, trying to retract out of her ass.

My wife climbed off of me. She sat on the couch beside my knees, panting and wiping sweat from her cheeks.

"Oh god. Thank you, Zachary!"

I made sure my face was aimed away from the camera while I rolled my eyes.

Our tubby patron climbed back into the frame, his cheeks patchy and eyes glazed over. He thanked us for letting him join in our fun, blew a kiss, and was gone.

"Jesus fucking Christ!" my wife groaned, waddling to the bathroom to unwheel a wad of toilet paper and clean up. "That was... It was..."

"Yeah," I agreed, hiding my face in my hands. "It was."

My career as a porn star had lasted thirty minutes and earned us fifty dollars. It had ended, not with a supernova blaze, but a whimper and a sigh, and a dick that seemed very happy to be soft and safe in boxer shorts once more.

Nowadays, when my wife goes to work, I take up my proper place in the kitchen, sponging dildos in the sink, packaging panties at the table, and wondering if Zachary ever came to his senses and shaved off that ridiculous neckbeard.

SHRINGI KUMARI
Garden of Vaginas

Samal came even closer, sighed loudly and blurted, "I like it when I do that to you." He flapped around as I stared at the giant art piece hanging on the wall of his pretentious little room. "Can a person have a pretentious penis?" I thought vacantly. "Of course, what am I even talking about," I mumbled into space. Samal wouldn't care if I were mumbling or lying dead, he would be busy — still flapping about. He undoubtedly has the most pretentious penis I have come across. His mind on the other hand, is that of a regular man — wanting to be important, liking absurd paintings, being interested in people with a particularly shaped nose (shaped like mine). A man with a very average penis having big penis dreams.

My body has played an important role in giving that penis its identity. I have impassively let him — do whatever the fuck he has wanted, while I have stared at paintings on the wall of his — well — pretentious little room.

I, on the other hand, have a penis that doesn't mean much or probably holds the exact amount of meaning any penis should hold. Very little.

I was born in a family of women. A fatherless child with a mother, four aunts (all of who I called *Ma* followed by their name), three sisters, many cousins (all of who I called sister followed by their name) and two grandmothers. I was born in a garden of vaginas — respectful, well groomed, protected under layers of clothing, deeply dug in an array of female bodies. Hidden from me and as far as I can say, from everyone. Even themselves. These South Asian women didn't mind my penis hanging about in their faces one bit, while girls my age were being tethered to undue social expectations. I did eventually get told — to put it in.

It had lost its adorableness rather abruptly, and was starting to become the wrinkly penis of a (to be) man. This had nothing to do with the penis in itself. It had everything to do with me. One of my mothers (aunts) caught me staring at my cousin and having the start of an erection. I was naked, my cousin was clothed, my aunt sad in a way that made guilt creep all over my body. In her eyes I had lost all of my innocence, forever. I never roamed around naked in the house again. That is also the day I lost all respect for my own body, specifically my stupid penis.

My cousin, sister Ajanya, was so perfect though — we were 12. She had soft hair, slow mannerisms, voice of a dream and the most hidden vagina of all hidden vaginas I have ever seen. Everyone knew she was the most attractive thing in the house, so was kept under special covers. Before the incident, I think I wanted to put my (addressed by adults as) baby penis into her mouth and watch her swallow me whole. I wanted to live inside her as much as I wanted her to live in me — flourish even. I wanted her to want all of me and I wanted me to never stop wanting any of her. I had a mad madness for her that probably aged my penis much faster than my many mothers would have liked. She was me. I was certain we were made of the exact same flesh, blood and bone. A very thin layer of exterior is all that made us different. Ajanya made me think of myself as a person with flowing blood, growing nails, falling hair, a person with an untouched nape and eyes that could look upwards once in a while. Come to think of it, as a child she made me feel adult things I can no longer feel as a grown up.

It was a sour night, some of my mothers had fought for hours over *saag* (a leaf-based dish) being served in the wrong china. They were entertaining a bunch of men who used to come every now and then — hang around, inspect the house, talk seriously in the courtyard, eat and leave. I never really cared who they were and they never really acknowledged my presence. We were mutually non-existent male beings dwelling in an all-woman universe for these undiscussed evenings. That night, Ajanya came to the rooftop where I was lingering, took off the *dupatta* (scarf) wrapped around her neck, and signaled me to hold it. I didn't. I instead took her right hand and jammed it into my pants. Her flesh touched my coy penis. I felt an erection in my mind, but my penis stayed limp. She tittered, "It is so weird," and started squishing my tiny dick. I walked away, crying, while she stood there giggling. I can't fathom what made her giggle like that. Since then, I have brewed a special kind of disgust for her; for all I know it is an excuse for me to not deal with my own actions and even more so to not deal with the idea of how that incident must have grown in her. What must I be to her — *I don't even want to put words to that thought.*

The past, at times, is just a shelf or some sort of a frame for us to hang the present on. A starting point. We went to the same college, studied the same irrelevant course, struggled with youth, went home in semester breaks taking the same train. We were to graduate as geologists together. We never really learned how to communicate, however, we did have bland sex ending in stifled orgasms

86

on a few occasions, in her neatly made hostel room. Childhood had gone, nothing was beautiful anymore, nothing could anymore be what it could have been. When we were back home during breaks, they teased us as if we were a couple. The thing that was so prohibited at 12, suddenly at 21 was not only okay, it was encouraged. My cousin, sister Ajanya, and I were allowed to be, wanting to be together. I don't think anybody would have openly approved of sex, but they would have been happy if we had said we wanted to get married. I was ashamed of our family. I was ashamed of our family and my body. Most of all, I was ashamed of Ajanya. How could she tolerate me, us, and how could she giggle (still) at what was being said. Or was she far beyond any of us? *Us...* our family was never an 'us'. It was always a mishmash of ill-fitting pieces, loosely glued together.

I am 36 now, Samal is my least exciting ex. We catch up once in a while. We first met at the day of Ajanya's wedding, about ten years ago. I had spent the morning pacing in my room, throwing clothes on my bed in a tantrum without an audience. I was at the edge of complete insanity — I did not know how to present myself. I did not know what clothes I could put on to hide my mental disarray. The wedding was scheduled for ten in the morning, I should have been ready to welcome the guests by at least eight. But I was in no state to assemble myself as a person and pour that into the casket of a sensible being. I took a shower and sat on my bed groaning while Ajanya was probably getting married. I did finally make an appearance, and it wasn't too late. I had not missed the event, although I was an hour late. I wore a blue shirt and jeans, playing it cool I suppose. My eyes were blood-shot-red, hair moderately wet and excessively combed, holding its place. I must have looked like an overworked brother of the bride who had spent all morning fixing things for everyone behind the scenes. I was prepared with excuses, but nobody asked. They were all moving around like butterflies, fidgeting with things and settling unpredictably.

Ajanya walked down the stairs, freshly prepared as a bride by a team of people. Our eyes met, hers instinctively moved away from my red gaze, and mine stuck. Oh my goodness, my heart fell, I distracted myself by making lame observations — she has painted herself like a clown. That beautiful woman who looked radiant after the most heavy of days, looked like an idiot. She had so much makeup on she was barely recognizable. My mind went on — blabbering away, trying to control my nerves in every which way. I could not get myself to see how beautiful she actually looked. For years, I had told myself that her beauty had faded on me the day she laughed while I cried on the rooftop. In college, she had looked pretty but distant, never as beautiful as she looked to me when we were children — the time when I wanted to live in her. Today, she looked like a clown, and that was it. One instant she looked like she could fly, in another she looked like she would collapse under the weight of the clothes, the makeup, the false hair and my peering eyes looking at her unblinkingly, thinking things. "Do you (still) love her?" said one of my mothers who must have seen me staring at her. "No, I don't, why did you put so much makeup on her?" Seera Ma looked at me with hopeless eyes and then at the sky, then at Ajanya and back at me, like a well-adjusted clock. "It will get easier," she said. "I think she is happy. You will learn to live with that. Someday you will realise it was a blessing to be born

into this family amongst all of us women. You will know
what you are to us and what you can be to Ajanya. She
looks beautiful, like always, but also like never before. Try
and have a good day today, if for nothing else, then for your
sister Ajanya."

I couldn't really say what made her say all of that, or
what she thought she meant. Could she have read my
scruffy soul? Within, I fell a deep fall, while standing there
uselessly. I did not have a good day, how could I, that
wedding, a seemingly pointless event was my final chance
to say a real word to my cousin sister. I think I ignored that
epiphany almost as unenthusiastically as I had had it. I
soaked in the chaos of the day, our household had always
been jam-packed with such chaotic pointless days. I still
don't know where we have all this money from, but I don't
dare ask questions as they lead to random, supposedly
poignant monologues like that of Seera Ma. In this
household of women, that I am someday supposed to be
grateful for, I have found only riddles. I have found only
corners to cry in and soulmates in walls of empty rooms.
But I can't complain, somewhere I have always known that
a house with men in it would only be worse.

I was about to say something back to Seera Ma,
something along the lines of, "Come on, of course I am
having a good day. All of you have made this day very very
special. I know I don't always say it but I do think we are
lucky to have had you look after us all these years." I
wouldn't have said all of it, and she wouldn't have believed
any of it anyway. She got busy though, she was greeting a
boy, or in her eyes a man in his early twenties, with way too
much respect deserved by any 20-something ever. I figured
he must be the groom's brother they had all been going

89

gaga about. Samal, Samal, oh Samal, poster child of our twisted culture. He was being courted by the coven for another of my sisters, which he seemed to be exceptionally excited about. Seera Ma introduced me as the man of the house, only half joking. I was astonished that she introduced me at all. I was usually left to do nothing and be nowhere. I think she wanted to assure Samal that our household had a token man that he could relate to. Samal was this young guy, drowning in attention, being just as flowing and temporal as he is now, ten years later. Only time would tell, age had nothing to do with his juvenile ideologies. We hit it off instantly, I was (am) a seeker of the pretentious. I was immediately attracted to Samal's immaculately shaven face and the worthy way in which he wiped his face with the back of his hand after stuffing his mouth with an entire *gulab-jamun* (sweet milk dumpling). *One of us,* the mothers must have internally rejoiced, in flawless harmony. I had been with men before, but none as far up their ass as him. He looked opulent, well read, and all those things that make a man desirable to the society and more importantly to himself. And I was a collector of men and women like these — like Ajanya, like Samal.

The wedding was a typical Hindu wedding where the bride and groom do things around a fire pretty much all day or night, day in this case. He was confused when I held his hand, while we were watching Ajanya go round a dimly lit fire. He took his hand away and looked at me with the stern disappointment of a father. A father I never had. I, like a mature child, let him take his hand away, in complete accordance. But a child I was, who wanted to have what he wanted to have. Like the smart child I always was, I dangled my hand next to his. It must have taken him 15 or more minutes to finally give in — touch my fingers like my patient childish self knew he would. What next — ease him into his gayhood? Let him hang there and pretend you were just being emotional while watching your cousin sister getting married? Guide him towards your once squished dick and take it away, like you did that night. I decided to follow my instincts and be the cruelest I could be. He obviously didn't want anyone to see us holding hands. I asked him if he wanted to go somewhere private. He nodded apprehensively. I took him to the only place I had wanted to be all day, Ajanya's bedroom, excessively dressed in strings of roses, for her first night of marital sex. I made Samal sit on Ajanya's husband's side of the bed. He was extremely impatient and said something like, "I am not into men, like, I love women, I love boobs." The gentlemanly poise of this guy was wearing off. I loved that. I loved watching his skin roll off him — his well-read-ness being reduced to "I love boobs." I don't remember, I must have laughed out loud, but I was at least laughing a lot within. I was winning some obscure game I was used to playing with people, peeling them off, layer after layer. I had peeled off Ajanya's splendor the day I ran away on the rooftop and left her giggling like a moron.

Samal shuffled stupidly. This was the point when I, at least to me, became superior to these perfect human beings. "I love boobs, too," I said like a mother. "I too love women, but that doesn't mean I don't like you. I don't want to pressure you into anything but I thought you would like to talk in private." He sat there, face in hands, and said, "I don't know, I don't even know you." I was smirking, I knew this game all too well. "Yes, you don't and I don't know you," I said, but I think I knew all about him by then.

"But we can help each other find ourselves out." That is probably the only true line I have ever spoken to him. He flapped about. Words were exchanged, clothes were removed, in no time, Samal — clothesless, shameless, defenceless — was parked in my asshole. While I lay, right where she would lie later that night, staring at the painting hanging on the wall of her pretentious little room.

SARAH EVANS
Scratching the Surface

Marianne reads out the party invitation, 'Bring a bottle and a plus one. Gatsby fancy dress.' She pulls a face. 'Not sure that's quite my thing.'

Her boyfriend of several months smiles wryly. 'Could be OK though? Something different.'

'Easy for you. Maybe I could go in pinstripe and fedora as well.' She'd never been a glitz and gloss sort of girl.

'Maybe I'd prefer to go as a flapper,' he says and she laughs. It takes a moment before she realises his face remains straight.

'Well I don't have any makeup for you to borrow.' This has to be a joke, right?

His skin flushes. 'Maybe I already have my own.'

His eyes meet hers fleetingly as he mumbles something about doing this at other parties and it being fun.

We remain sitting, Robert in the armchair, me with my feet curled up at one end of the sofa. I shake myself from sunken thoughts, re-emerging into the present, aware of the noises of the house, the clunking of cooling radiators, floorboards creaking overhead, the open and close of doors and ensuing silence. I glance up.

Robert's eyes meet mine, blue and opaque. He half-smiles, but there's no enthusiasm to it. 'What d'you feel?' he asks, voice low.

'In shock, I guess.' Understatement of a lifetime.

'You?'

'The same.'

'I just hadn't...' I say.

'Neither of us had.'

'No.'

'I thought, well, I mean, we'd talked before about...'

'That he might be gay.' I think what a relief that would be. 'D'you think he's really thought it through?' I ask.

'He says he has. It's not something he'd say without thinking long and hard.'

'I know. But he's still so young, can he really know that about himself?'

'Twenty-two. The age you were when we met.'

It is hard to reconcile how grown up I felt then with how young my son seems now. I have changed my view on so many things over the years, but not on anything fundamental. By early teens, I knew my sexuality, my lack of religion, the leftwards tilt of my politics, and the direction for my career. I think how strong my sense of self has always been. How unshakeable.

She calls round for him that evening, hoping he'll have had a change of heart, her own heart jolting as the door opens onto a glamorous vision, in which she both recognises him and doesn't.

'I didn't know you had a twin,' she says. The best, the only, option, seems to be to make light of things.

'Rhiannon,' he says, his voice softer than usual. 'Will I do?'

She forces a laugh. 'A bit too convincing. We should get going.'

She's made her best token effort, a knee length shift

dress, a black feather headband, and matching feather boa looped through her elbows. As always, her shoes are low and practical. They head out. It isn't far, not in normal circumstances. 'Are you alright walking in those?' She gestures down at his ankle-breaker heels, wondering where on earth he found them in his size, how he had known where to go.

'I'm fine.' And unnervingly, he is, his hips swaying in a cat-walk rhythm that can only have come with practice.

She absorbs him in passing glances. Makeup expertly applied, curled hair held back in a sparkly feather headband, long fingerless gloves, a silver sequined strap-dress with hip-tassels, the bodice fitting tightly over his fake breasts. They walk in silence and she wonders if he's regretting his choice, is all set to ask if he'd rather skip the party and go home. Yet his head is held high and when a couple of workmen wolf-whistle, he laughs and waves and all the past months of slowly getting to know one another seem to evaporate into the evening air.

'He says he's always known.' Robert echoes what Ryan has just told us. *I didn't just wake up and decide this,* our son said.

Our son. From that first ultrasound, when we pored over what lay between his legs, that is how we have viewed him. It's the first question everyone asks about your newborn: boy or girl? The congratulations cards are colour coded. Even when you hope to avoid the worst of the conventional thinking, gender is always there.

He, his, him, himself, son, boy, man, Ryan. All the words we will need to excise and replace.

'Remember as a little boy, he always liked teddies and

prams, more than guns and trains,' Robert continues. 'He preferred playing with girls. And loved dressing up.'

'Lots of kids do those things.'

We thought we were being progressive, not forcing him into narrow roles, letting him follow his inclination. Did we make a mistake, encouraging traits best left dormant? Is there something we did, or failed to do? I look at my husband's slender fingers, his narrow shoulders, dark hair curling against his pale neck; in the semi-dark he has such a look of Ryan. 'You weren't exactly the most boyish of boys. Liked books much more than football.' And I was never a girly girl.

Robert's eyes are cast downwards, long eyelashes shielding his gaze. His mouth – soft and full – is slightly parted with words he cannot find.

'What does it really mean though?' I continue. My whole life I have shunned the negative *isms* and phobias. Sexism, racism, homophobia. Transphobia is the latest addition to that list and clearly gender dysphoria is something some people – other people – feel. 'Do you know anyone?' I ask. 'Anyone transgender?' I test out the shape of the sounds in my mouth.

'Not knowingly,' Robert says.

'Me neither.' My mind does a scan of colleagues and casual acquaintances: might I be making the wrong assumption somewhere? My ex-boss loved doing the drag thing at office parties. That isn't the same. *Cross-dressing, transvestite, drag queen, transgender, transsexual, two-spirit, genderqueer, non-binary*: there is a spectrum of language I have yet to fully tease out.

The evening passes in a nightmare blur in which everything she thought she understood feels as flimsy as her companion's shimmering dress. She downs several glasses of gin martini, wincing at the bitter taste, desperate to pretend she's having a good time. Their friends are dressed flamboyantly, full of wide-eyed laughter, all seeming to enjoy the joke and she wonders what is wrong with her, what has happened to her sense of humour. All evening she watches the shy, gentle boy she has been slowly, steadily falling for transform before her eyes into this glittering livewire of a girl, chatting and laughing with strangers, keen to outdo everyone on the dance floor. He seems to shine and sparkle and the more he does so the more morose she becomes and she wonders what this says about her. About them.

'D'you think he's really fixed on it?' I ask.

'I don't know. He says he's wanted to say something for years.'

I've something to tell you, Ryan said earlier. He looked so nervous, the maturity of his college years falling away.

Good news or bad? Robert asked.

That depends on how you view things.

'Well why didn't he?'

Robert remains quiet. We both remember the answer Ryan provided to that question.

Because you'd have told me I was too young to know and insisted that I was wrong about myself. That wouldn't have helped.

And if a mother cannot help her child then what kind of mother does that make her?

'He says he's getting counselling,' Robert says.

'But what kind of counselling?' The sort that will

97

support and bolster his views or something that might robustly question him?

Robert shrugs and I hate his air of resignation. Did we challenge Ryan enough right now? Were we too accepting, too fearful of seeming dismissive, or politically incorrect, or of hurting his feelings? But how else should liberal, loving parents respond?

'It's a long process. He's only at the start. Plenty of time for him to change his mind.' Robert provides the voice of reason. I feel constrained by this careful show of neutrality and wish he would express a stronger view, giving me permission to do the same.

'It's not that easy,' I say. 'What damage might be done in the meantime? And what if the process is self-reinforcing, making it difficult to backtrack?' Questions churn. Likely this merely reveals my ignorance, but still it seems odd to me that in the modern world, forgiving in so many ways, a person cannot be whosoever they choose without the need for medical procedures, for physical refashioning, with the attendant risks and possible pain. There is no problem, surely, for a man to be feminine in his sensitivities, occupation, interests, desires. Why this need to be feminine in his body too? I think of the body I knew so intimately once, his baby form no different in its essentials to his sister's, other than for one important detail, the undeniable biological fact. The boy growing, until, aged six, he insisted he wanted to bath on his own. The teenager, so awkwardly self-conscious and fiercely private.

Everyone thinks it's all about penises, our son said. *It's like nobody can think beyond that.* There's no need for me to know the full details of what he might – or might not – plan. Yet I'm his mother; surely I ought to know.

'I've had enough,' Marianne says, though the evening is still in full swing. They share a taxi and though she'd expected to sleep over at his, she pleads a headache and says she'll see him tomorrow. He leans in towards her, but she cannot bear to kiss his lipsticked lips and deflects them onto her cheek. And as the cab draws up outside his house-share, she turns to him and, in a low voice, she says, 'Never again. I don't want to see you like this again.' He doesn't respond, but his face is pale beneath the slashes of blusher enhancing his cheekbones and in his eyes she reads a kind of defeat. The spark that had flamed all evening is extinguished.

'Do you understand it?' I ask and distant memories scratch as Robert looks back at me with impenetrable eyes. He simply shakes his head.

'He's an intelligent person,' Robert says eventually. 'An adult.'

D'you think I haven't thought about each and every objection you might make? D'you think I'd really do this if I didn't need to? Ryan's words replay. He looked so defenceless as he pleaded with us to understand.

Explain it to me, I want to say to Robert, but the sell-by for that conversation was so long ago and besides, it isn't the same.

I always swore that I would respect my child's choices. That, once they were of age, I wouldn't try and second guess my kids or assume that I knew best. I was determined not to repeat my parents' mistakes, but this proves harder than I'd ever have expected.

Mum and Dad were strident in their religion. Aged

fourteen, I battled them openly by refusing to go to church, but mostly my battles were won in secret. They had no power to stop me having boyfriends and going on the Pill. Later, when Robert visited, they insisted on separate bedrooms, but they couldn't police the midnight tiptoeing over the creaking boards on the landing, the silent sex, to which transgression brought an added thrill. They disapproved, fiercely, of Robert and I living together. At no point did their opinions matter. We were simply driven ever further apart, until with time their positions softened; even my parents were swept along with the tide of changing times.

But not this far.

'Oh God,' I say. 'How will we tell Mum and Dad?' Whatever my concerns, I cannot bear the thought of other people judging my child. Mum and Dad will be the worst, but how well, really, will others respond?

'Ryan will have to figure that out himself.'

'Leila,' I say, '*herself*.' Deliberately, I test out the name and pronoun, trying to get my brain to process this thing that doesn't make any sense. It is going to have to. Tomorrow my son will come down to breakfast wearing women's clothes and makeup. The hair he usually scoops back in a ponytail will hang loose. *I'd like you to start calling me Leila.* He had some photos on his phone. *So you get the idea.* The images were disconcerting, the face I know so well transformed, recognisable and not. *Of course the effect will be much better once I start hormone treatment, but that won't be for a while; I have to live as a woman first.*

Once, not *if*.

They never spoke about it afterwards. She was so convinced that she was right, dismissing this flashy act, because it did not fit with her view of the world, or of him. He returned to his former wry understatement, the slight guardedness which she found so attractive. The next time she got an invite to a fancy dress party, she tore it up and threw the scraps away.

We continue sitting in the semi-dark, the room cooling, fragments of the earlier conversation replaying, neither of us knowing what more there is to say, both of us getting steadily tireder, yet what point is there in going to bed where we will fail to sleep. 'He says he's already told Bella,' I say. 'And Ewan and Chris.' I listen to myself and self-correct in my head; learning to use *she* is going to take time and practice.

His sister, cousins, friends are all cool with it, my child said. Hurt pulses, that he would speak to others before us, building up his sandbags of support. His generation aren't fazed by these things, isn't that what all the newspaper articles and social surveys claim? *The position of women. Sexual liberation. Racial equality. Gay rights. Secularism.* Fast-held certainties shift in ways previously unimaginable and the older cohort either changes too, or at least they die out in time.

But the current world, the here and now, consists of more than the hip crowd at his modern university. Sensationalist headlines fill the newspaper hoardings. Trans people are at greater risk of violence. They are at risk of self-harm. My heart squeezes painfully tight. I can't protect him from the former, but acceptance by those they love is the best defence against the latter.

'You always wanted daughters,' I say and both of us attempt to smile.

We sit in the darkening silence. I dig fingernails into the pads of my thumbs. Ryan is still the baby, child, teenager, youth whom I have always loved; my greatest wish is that he – she – find happiness. I cannot foresee the best route to that, just as my parents did not have the roadmap for me. I accept this and yet it is so hard.

Robert moves, the chair creaking. He stands, stretches. 'We should get some sleep,' he says.

I feel as if I will never rest again.

'I'll be up in a bit,' I say and I watch the slender line of him as he pads across the room.

I sit in the dark and memories replay, the thing I have not dwelt on for so long, those players in a different life. It was never important, was it? That awful Gatsby party.

Robert never shone or sparkled that way again.

My thoughts circle round that aberration of an incident from long ago, which is not the same as Ryan, though it triggers a parallel gut-tight discomfort. I can remember my conviction – *it isn't natural* – but can no longer re-inhabit it. Isn't *natural* only what culture defines? Only now do I wonder whether, times when Robert is alone, he brings out a secret stash of makeup, drapes himself with scarves, perches on heels and stares at his looking glass image, imagining a different self who occupies a different world, thinking back to that one glorious evening when he was not himself, or was most himself, how can I know. The cold of night shivers through and I hug myself tight.

I think of being me, the layer upon layer of complexity to my thoughts, fantasies, longings, and of the splinters which I allow to surface. I think how little of another person you can truly understand, how you can live alongside someone for decades and all you know of them is surfaces, you never really touch their secret self.

MOLLY MCLELLAN
Field

It's common knowledge that men, a majority of men, like to boast that they think with two heads: the one on their neck and the one in their pants. I can confirm this is a lie. Men rarely, if ever, listen to us. John sure didn't listen to me. I mean look at me; I'm a bloody mess, abandoned in a field to die. Maybe it's for the best. I shudder to think of the damage I could've continued to do if I were still attached to him. The cool breeze is filtering through this long grass, every so often parting the large blue green blades so I can see the stars. I suppose there could be a worse way for me to meet my fate. I honestly can't remember if I've ever seen stars like this before. The mass of them up there in the dark, shimmering, dancing as if the breeze is wafting them back and forth instead of the grass; it gives one hope, even if you are just a penis.

How, you may ask, does a penis end up in a field slowly bleeding to death? The simplest answer is, a girl. A girl I would happily do this for, all over again.

I remember the first time I saw her, her blonde hair blowing in a breeze similar to the one shifting the grass around me now. It was a manmade breeze, a fan in the corner of a muggy hot Virginia apartment, but it made her hair dance the same way the stars gracefully move above me. I will hold no grudge towards her. I will miss her, but I will only hope the best for her. After everything we have been through, I have to hope for the best, but I'm getting ahead of myself.

* * *

When John was younger he had a fetish with me as I imagine most teenage boys do with their penises. I was 'let out', so to speak, so often I thought I would never get a break. I didn't know then exactly what got him so excited, what got him to encourage me to rise. I couldn't read his mind after all. But when he first saw her, I got a sense of what he must've been wanting all those years.

He seemed to me to be like most men we encountered. I would hear their muffled voices deepening with age, time passing so that John's interest in me began to fade. Mostly I came out so he could relieve himself. Public restrooms were my favorite place to be let out back then, in that period of time when he went from a teenager to a young man: from groping for me to groping at women who squealed or giggled at his failed attempts in luring their hands towards me. I was glad only a few were brave enough to come close to touching me. Their fumbling inexperienced hands felt less than great compared to the rhythmic and perfunctory treatment I was used to in John's hands.

No, it was public washrooms I preferred. Till I saw her, till I encountered the loveliness of her, it was the brisk cold of public toilets that enthralled me. Depending on John's state of intoxication we would sometimes linger longer, giving me more pleasure than he knew. To be released from the stifling confines of his pants was a wondrous treat, especially as the cold crisp bathroom air greeted me and the pressure from behind burst forth. In those brief seconds, occasionally minutes, I would get a sneak peek at others like myself; and sometimes, rarely, a

105

quick conversation. I think what enthralled me the most was how different we each are. Not just in color, size, and form, but not all of us even identify as male! How strange and magnificent it must be to know you're something else when the whole world is reflecting a different idea on you. I have wished for many years I was something different than what John made me, but the truth is penises have very little to do with what they are forced into. Although I imagine, rather I hope, that some of us are treated better, that others fare better.

Before I saw her, it had been a muffled voice I met first: different from the others, not piercing or shrill, but tranquil, calm, almost tentative in its every response to John. As if she suspected even back then a power behind him, a power that would change us both, alter us forever. Her voice trapped John and me; we were both consumed by it. When he would bring me out then for our ritual meetings, I imagined only her voice and presumed John was doing the same.

It was months before I finally met her. Some sort of procession had taken place that day. I was smashed into a softer fabric, black as night but not nearly as stifling as John's usual jeans. There was a lot of repetition of words I could barely make out, but I could hear her voice, bright with excitement and it almost made me stand on edge. Somehow John kept me down. Then the evening came, the whir of manmade wind pushing against the pants that encased me, buzzed all around. Then there she was. Her hair golden, falling in loose curled tendrils around the most beautiful face I had ever seen.

Her lips were a coral pink, pursed together in a quaint smirk that instantly froze me. Her eyes twinkled like the stars above me do now, glittering back at me with so much love I couldn't help but fall head over heels for her. Her thighs were plump and the softest thing I ever grazed across, and inside her was a beautiful gift I could hardly begin to describe. How I wish I could forever be with her, tender like that night was. Patient at first, dotted with slight fumbling, eventually a rhythm struck up between her and John and I was the exquisite tool to her pleasure. How I wish it could've stayed that way forever.

It was the second time I saw her that I found out the truth about John, that power behind him that she had been wise to be cautious of, but that she had eventually learned to ignore. She was lying, still and quiet, her breathing soft, a slight adorable snore to her exhales. John was stumbling as he gripped me hard, a sure-fire sign of his intoxication. Usually our ritual in this state was extremely brief, he was too fired up to last much longer than a few seconds. Otherwise sleep would overcome him and he would pass out. But he had never been in this state with her before. I figured he was simply using her image to finish the job; I could easily see why he would want to. Her face in the moonlight had a particular paleness to it that caused her skin to appear almost translucent, like I imagine a white petal from a rose might look as it drifts on clear crisp water. Soft and tender, a slight sparkle to it. But John had other intentions.

That first time was a blur for me, it all happened so fast, and I pray it was a blur for her too. In seconds he was on her and I became something I will always regret, something I will always curse. I became John's weapon, his prize-winning instrument of torture, and he laid into her relentlessly that night. I tried my hardest to come down, to somehow become limp, it was useless, this only seemed to spur him on further. His rage increasing as he bashed me about till I came back up. Eventually I gave in, hoping at least it would end quickly. It didn't.

The next morning she couldn't bear to look at me. She would never touch me, never stroke me tenderly again, not till the night she freed me, freed us both.

* * *

The stars are starting to fade; the grass is going limp as a light begins to grow on the very distant horizon. I can hear a rustling from time to time as if footsteps are approaching. I pray they aren't. How odd for a penis to become so religious in its last moments on Earth. But if you knew, if you knew how many nights I had to be an unwilling participant to his outbursts, to John's every whim. How he enjoyed her screams, her protests, her thrashing. I'm sure you would understand why lying here bleeding to death is a much better choice. Even if I had been foolish enough to think it could end another way. The breeze has completely ceased now and I can feel the heat of the day starting to build. The light growing on the horizon seems to be shifting the grass so it is going rigid, turning to a darkened brown. I remember once in a brief public washroom appearance we encountered a poet's penis. He was a rather eloquent yet stout fellow, and his penis reflected him as if it were a mirror, albeit fleshier. I remember the penis seemed to be glowing in the blue manmade light of the bathroom, the veins pulsing as the poet spurted on.

"Nothing can hide from the light of day, how I love the light of day."

I remember the way John shook me and stuffed me away, his arrogance getting the better of him again. He scoffed and muttered the man was a drunken fool who shouldn't consume so much rum in one sitting. I believed John at the time, after all, the light rarely found me. Turns out I was wrong. The poet had a point. There is very little that can hide from the light of day. John was not little though.

* * *

Every morning he would rise as if nothing had happened, as if the bruises on her wrists and hips were fixed birthmarks that always existed in his mind. Her voice became quieter and colder with each passing encounter. How I longed to explain to her that I wished I could stop him, that I wished I could give her relief from his onslaught of horror. But it didn't matter; I learned quickly that even if I managed to stay limp despite his beatings and anger, he would only find another tool, another instrument to torment her with. Then I was left completely defenseless as I was forced to watch his circus of pain. At least if I was involved I could try, try my best to push out all the sounds, the feelings, and try to bring John to a brief end. I spent weeks desperately trying to communicate to the two orbs which hung on either side of me, desperately seeking a way for them to hurry the process that was John's end to these nights. They were useless to say the least.

I wished I had a connection to the other head, to the part of John that seemed to be calling the shots. If there were a connection, trust me I would've found it. After realizing the uselessness of the orbs, I spent day and night searching for a link in me to any other part of John that could get a message to his other head. Those days were torturous and long, as I knew the inevitable was coming. It was only the very rare evening that John drank himself into such a stupor he could barely make it through the front door, usually choosing to collapse on the couch. I would lie, pressed into the fabric, dreaming of when I had been softly pressed against the small of her back as she slept, her soft skin soothing me.

I know the pain was worse for her, I could feel it, hot and burning around me till it ended. I will never pretend it was worse for me, I will only wish every day that I had known how to do what she accomplished, I will only wish I had made that tie to John's other head, found a way to that blade myself, ended it for her myself.

* * *

Daylight is now nearly above me, and the sun is hot today. The grass lends little relief as it is now fully bristled and erect in this intense heat. I can feel the last of the blood seeping from me, it won't be long now till there's nothing left of me except for shriveled drying skin around slack greying flesh. The rustling from before was a few field mice, which had little to no interest in me. When I tried to enquire where I might be they clearly had no knowledge of the phallic tongue. I suppose it doesn't matter where I spend my last minutes on this Earth, I just wish I could tell her I was sorry, wish I had had the chance to explain that night the pure joy and awe I felt as she gripped me tight for the last time. How splendid it was.

It was like any night; John was drunk again and stumbling towards what was now less a bedroom and more a prison cell. At least that night it was brief, he had managed to get so worked up that barely any time had passed before she was relieved of him and the awful creature I had been forced to become. As I lay there, next to her but not touching her, I began to feel doomed. My years of trying to communicate to the other head were fruitless and it seemed her suffering and anguish was my only future. I remember feeling that if I could weep I would. That's when she rose and stood at the end of the bed. This wasn't unusual. Once John's snores reached a symphonic level she seemed to feel safe enough to rise most nights. Safe in the assured nature of his state that his body wouldn't be rising till the light of day shone on him. Trying its best to reveal his horrible nature, his disgusting state of mind. Like my own attempts at ceasing his behavior, the light was futile in its attempts.

She rose that night though; the trembling that usually followed her breathing and steps was quiet tonight. I watched as her pale form slinked out of the room. The plumpness that had once shifted and fallen around her hips and thighs was now gone: a skeletal frame replacing those curves. What was once plentiful and filled with warmth was cold, brittle, a harsh line cutting through the night as it strode out of the room. I longed to follow her, to comfort her.

I heard the tap run then, desiring to be in the coolness of the kitchen next to her, soaking up the freshness that comes with that rushing of cold water as it hits metal and fills glass. I could hear her sipping slowly on the water, her breath steadying. Then nothing, not even the creak or crack of floorboards as she shifted from one bare foot to the other. I waited, trying desperately not to get too excited, not to get too worried. I knew if I rose she wouldn't return. I revolted her in that state. I needed to stay calm, to hope she would return so I could try to somehow be there for her.

Waiting for what seemed like days, I felt the pulse behind me start to quicken and braced myself for what was coming. All it would take was one glance through the doorframe and she would choose the couch instead of the bed. She would choose to stay up all night on that stained and revolting couch instead of trying to rest, trying to find some moment of quiet peace she so deserved. How wrong I was.

She glanced alright and that smirk, that quaint coral smirk from before, dotted her face briefly. Her eyes were locked on me, that smirk was for me. I couldn't help myself; I went more rigid than the grass that surrounds me now. At last, I thought, at last I have my chance, my chance to explain myself. A fool is defined as a person who acts unwisely or imprudently. Believe me when I say it doesn't just relate to a person. I was so locked on her gaze that I never saw the glint of stainless steel in her hand. I'm sure if another penis was ever to get the chance to ask me how I managed to miss an eight-inch carving knife headed my way I would sound like the world's biggest fool when I answered: you don't know what her gaze was like.

It was brief, so quick in fact that I didn't feel pain till at least an hour into our car ride. She separated my flesh from his in an instant. The cold blade felt more refreshing than any brilliant bathroom I had ever beheld. And her grip, it wasn't tender, nor was it harsh, it was simply what needed to be done to free her, to free me, to free us both from his atrocities.

I half expected him to burst upright, to fling himself at us both. The woman whose suffering brought him life and the penis that betrayed him to run away with her. I expected him to know it was my idea at the very start, to suspect me from the very beginning. To want to take his rage out on me right away. That he would somehow know all along the connection I was trying to make, the ways in which I was trying to undermine and end him. But all he did was flinch, had I not been so terrified of his vengeance I probably would've missed it. The small shudder in his hips, and then a loud snore, followed by a scratching at what had once been there.

She wasted no time; we were out the door and in the car before I really had a chance to absorb it all, the whole picture, the whole scenario. All I could focus on was her grip, firm, steady, and so sure of itself. I half expected her to fling me into the backseat like some coat or purse once we got to the car. If I was lucky enough maybe the passenger seat.

In John's car that night, the muggy summer air clung to the insides of metal surrounded by cheap fabric. I tightened in anticipation of the rough feeling of scratchy cloth against my oozing bloodied skin. She didn't let me go though. She held fast as she turned the keys in the ignition and set off through the downtown of that small Virginia town we had both called hell for those many years.

Once streetlights began to fade, darkness surrounded us both like the kind warm arms of a longtime friend. Her grip remained fastened around me and I couldn't believe my luck. All those horrible nights, those hours and minutes of brutal violence that surrounded us both felt like a blink, like a curtain was quickly drawn. Separating us from them in a split second. How could she know? I thought over and over again of my actions, of my attempts to end her misery. Had I made my own torment clear? Had she known all along I was the unwilling weapon to John's own house of horrors? I stayed in that state for what felt like forever, and I will always be grateful for being that fool in that moment. How I toiled over our every encounter, how I wished to cry out to her that I loved her and would never be able to repay her. All she did was hold fast to me as the darkness continued and the car burned on down a highway that I was convinced would lead us to safety. To a life together where I could once more be what she needed, be what she deserved, make sure that the rest of her life was filled with love and pleasure and nothing short of happiness. How wrong a fool can be.

* * *

As the night consumed us both and my thoughts consumed me, she rolled down a window. The cool breeze whipping at her hair so that it brushed against me. What was once solid gold blonde was now flecked with grey streaks that danced in the dark like the ghosts of every experience John had forced on her. I watched as they floated around me. So ridiculous to think that had I enough love for her I could erase those ghosts. As she sped on, the wind got colder, the night darkened to a purple black, the headlights of the car barely making out the ditches and fields that rose up to meet us from time to time. Tears began to form on her cheeks, soft pearly drops of water dripping from the corners of her eyes, spilling like a trembling creek across her skin. How I

114

wished I could join her so she would know my feelings matched hers. As the tears fell harder her grip grew tighter and I longed to grip her back, to make her feel the comfort she made me feel in that moment. It would all be okay, I kept trying to say; all of this is now in the past.

I didn't anticipate brakes being hit, the sudden thrash of us both against the steering wheel when she slammed her foot into the brake pedal. Her breathing quickened and the worst most selfish thought of all went through my head; please don't take us back there.

* * *

She of course had no intention of ever taking us back or ever taking me onwards with her. How thoughtless I was of everything that had taken place between us. Of course, she didn't see me as anything other than a weapon she had to rid her oppressor of. It was a big and brilliant leap towards her freedom, and for that I will always admire her strength and perseverance. I will always wish though, that I could've at least told her how in awe I am of her and that I never wished any of this on her. To explain how I longed to end it years ago for her, and mostly how in my own way, I loved her.

When the tears truly began to run and her breathing became labored, she screamed, a shrill cry that I'm sure was heard the world round by anyone who has ever had to fight for their freedom. Even now I wish I could reiterate that noise, feel its power, its release, but it wasn't for me to have. All the freedom in the world belonged to her, that cry of war ending, of the battle over, that was for her alone. And with that cry I was flung into a field, a field of stars and blue grass that has now turned harsh and brown all around me as I decay into the ground beneath me. And I wouldn't change this night for anything in the world.

Her taillights drifted on down the road, and as their red light left me to be engulfed by the cold night, I felt more loved than ever before. Now I'm dying in a field, in probably one of the strangest ways a penis can die, but I feel loved for the first time, because I am free. I wonder how many of us can say that, especially in these circumstances.

The sun is at its peak and the heat beats down on me relentlessly. I hope wherever she is she feels the same sun, the same heat, the same sense of love and freedom. I hope someday she'll find everything she so deserves and more. My skin is beginning to shrivel and the last of the blood has begun to leave me. The golden sun above reminds me of her hair, the white wisps of clouds dancing around it like the ghosts tangled in the tresses of her hair. I know a wind will come and sweep them from her strands of silken gold just as the wind is already shifting the clouds to give me one last breath of pure cold air.

TOBSHA LEARNER
Homage
An anecdote and true story

I was between two significant relationships, the man I thought I was going to marry and the man I'm married to now. It was a strange time, one of those periods in life where you're dating like crazy, kissing a lot of frogs and somewhere in the quagmire of one night stands, short (usually emotionally abusive) flings you become vaguely aware that your judgement is not what it should be.

The break-up had been brutal. And, to my own surprise, I'd had a total emotional and mental meltdown, compounded by the fact I was really in the last chance stages of my fertility. Losing the man I thought I was going to marry meant I'd lost the chance to have a child naturally unless I was to conceive by arrangement and go it alone. As the child of a single parent, and as a struggling writer, I wasn't prepared to do that.

I'd been living in LA when the first significant relationship broke down and the emotional aftermath had driven me back to Sydney into the arms of my siblings and old associates, a city I hadn't lived in for just under a decade, so there was also a cultural and social adjustment I hadn't calculated in the move. But then there was the bonus of easy-going uncomplicated sexuality of the Australian male.

I started dating a very tall and ridiculously beautiful younger man. As perfectly portioned as most of his body was, he was somewhat smaller than average, which on such a large frame is more of a visual paradox. I always get this image of a conveyor belt with God doling out the various body parts as he churns out the next generation of clay 'Adams'. And it's always struck me how often the wrong men get given the wrong penis – small on tall and vice versa. Don't get me wrong I'm not a size queen and it's always made very little difference sexually. Beautiful Bad Boy was a great lover, but this personal quirk of his is relevant to the story.

He was the kind of creature both women and men would do that rather annoying head swirl whenever he entered a room: Beautiful rather than handsome and very heterosexual, although that didn't seem to deter both gay and straight men acknowledging his allure. He was also a player, no surprise there. But to be fair he was a player after a long monogamous marriage and we'd been friends before we were lovers so I don't have that alibi of claiming I had no idea what I was getting into. Remember this was a long time before #MeToo, and players back then still had a kind of heroic cache as well as a fatal attraction. Now they tend to end up in court.

I remember reading once that there is an anthropological reasoning behind why women like promiscuous non-committal men – the same trait exists in animals – fish even. Female guppies like to mate with the males that other female guppies show the most sexual interest in – probably because these bad boy guppies are displaying genetic traits that are more desirable than the other weedier males – more colourful tails, more aggression, etc.

Certainly I have noticed over the years that some of the most unreliable bad boys – both emotionally and financially

– end up having the most children with the most number of women, often not paying a dime toward their upkeep, so there must be something to it.

Sexy guppy or no sexy guppy, Bad Boy and me were having a great time in the sack. Despite a slight lack of intellectual stimuli and trying to convince myself otherwise I'd begun to fall a little – the usual trap of thinking you are the one woman who will miraculously transform a commitment phobe and sex addict's behaviour, because, sisters, you're the *one*. Yeah right. I should have known better, in fact I did know better but he was very beautiful, funny and smelt great – a deadly combo.

It was at this time I was approached by an old theatre colleague who asked me to put in a submission for a comedy festival of short plays. I was excited to have some work back on the stage so I started to brainstorm with myself. This usually involves a lot of daydreaming, tricking my subconscious into pulling together a lot of seemingly disparate threads into a narrative or image.

I'd written plays and short stories about womanisers before, and I was certainly more than comfortable with male characterisation.

I can't quite remember how the idea came to me, but I suspect it was a combination of the absurdity of some of those hyper-real vibrators and the disconnection a lot of men experience between their heart and penis – erections at odds times, sudden inexplicable impotence and so on. But also the notion of penis as symbol – from artist Keith Haring to 'icon penis' as sex power graffiti – from cave man to toilet block. All of these themes swilled around my imagination until an actual vision hit me like a visitation from Priapus himself.

I told my producer mate I had a brilliant comedic idea but the only way it would work was if he could provide me with an excellent costume designer who could make me the most realistic costume possible. Once he had reassured me this was possible I pitched him my idea.

Named *Homage* – as in homage to the male gender – I wanted to stage a ten-minute monologue from the perspective of the penis of a porn star who'd just had the epiphany (in the middle of a filmed orgy) that he needed emotional intimacy to continue to perform sexually. In other words, the counter opposite of what is expected of the male species, and particularly male porn stars. From that moment in the play both penis and porn star are fatally and professionally flaccid and at war with each other. The rest of the monologue is the penis/porn star's poignant journey to find emotional intimacy and finally an emotional love that is integrated with Eros.

This often fraught dynamic between sex and intimacy was a theme I'd written about before but the idea of a male sex professional having a sudden and unwelcome integration of both heart and cock struck me as both comic and tragic. Subtext: Is it possible to continue to objectify one's sexuality without emotional consequences?

I also had in mind the kind of bawdy Aristophanes Greek comedy like *The Frogs* or *Lysistrata*, only starring one performer, and the thought of what one could achieve with a seven foot hyper-realistic penis hopping around a stage in terms of physical comedy was irresistible. But what I was going for required realism not some grotesque Disney version of a cock. It could only work if the costume was uber real – the 'straight' guy in the gag so to speak.

Hence my request for a really good costume designer,

not to mention the difficulty of casting the poor bastard in the penis suit.

Luckily the producer loved the pitch and recommended a female director who was also a choreographer; another essential as the actor would need strong direction in movement and in the blocking on stage of what was essentially a one hander (pun intended).

I wrote the play and we cast a lovely man in his early thirties with a reputation as a brilliant Shakespearian actor, handsome and well over six foot, with a good sense of humour and craft.

To his credit he was totally comfortable with the idea of playing a talking penis, I suspect he thought it would look interesting on the CV – but it was a good script and had some real bones theatrically both in terms of the emotional journey of the protagonist and the physical comedy. And as it was a new untried play, as playwright I was required to work closely with the director, costume designer and the actor.

One memorable meeting with the costume designer was when we had to decide whether the costume was to be *cut* or *uncut*? I have to put this in context; most Australian men of a certain age were automatically circumcised (the country took on the custom from the Americans) regardless of religion. But the politics of circumcision aside, there was a far more practical argument in terms of the costume for *cut*. This was a practical decision not an aesthetic one (try explaining that when cornered after a show by five disgruntled male audience members). Basically we needed to work out where to place the face of the actor. A foreskin would only complicate the line of the costume so *cut* it was. The actor's face was to peep out between the split in the glans on the underside, the most visually absurd placement possible, but also the most obvious.

The rehearsals got underway. They were taking place in a community centre that boasted a rather shabby stage and auditorium with rooms leading off in which the various local support groups would meet, which meant they had to cross the auditorium to reach their meetings.

Groups like Abused Wives, Anorexia, Narcotics Anonymous and Alcoholics Anonymous would trail mournfully across the hall; indifferent, too stressed or dazed to pay much attention to the tall actor prancing across the stage watched by three women; one interrupting with directions, until the dress rehearsal.

The costume worked beautifully, the seven-foot penis was both strangely cute and poignant at the same time. The actor was eased into the penis suit that was completely enclosing, a zip up the back, two large testicles concealing his legs from the shin down so that he could at least walk, or rather hobble and hop. His face peeping out between the split down the underside of the glans was sheer visual bathos. As soon as he began tentatively hopping around the stage, practising all kinds of tumescence, flaccidly 'pointing' at the audience, the director, the costume designer and myself – all female – we were literally in hysterics for about five minutes before being able to settle down to the serious business of the dress rehearsal.

There was also something profoundly primal about a seven-foot free-range penis. One is reminded of the erotic joy of Shinto and images of huge wooden phalli being paraded around Japanese cities without any of the Judeo-Christian squeamishness many of us westerners are afflicted with. Or the glorious erotic murals of Pompeii – again comedic, erotic, and satirically and anatomically absurd but still infused with a nudge-nudge, wink-wink joyfulness. The sheer exuberance of being human and fallible could, arguably, be encapsulated in the foibles of the penis. Antics that are often beyond the control of its 'owner', leading to mortifying embarrassing faux pas, for example an erection is always good for unwittingly exposing who one might really desire, as opposed to who one *should* desire (i.e. Margaret Thatcher, the dental assistant who looks like your gran, the shop manikin in that strangely hot mankini).

And there is also the female heterosexual gaze – from that perspective an erection is a wondrous almost magical event. It is the unknown, something that will always remain 'Other' and, held tenderly, can conjure up a myriad of emotions: from erotic to reassuring, and all the shades in between, but I digress, back to that rather shoddy community hall and the rickety stage.

So the actor was in the middle of his monologue, waddling around on his balls, exploring all manner of physical gags and comedy inherent in his actual stance – from erect to supine – and the audience, us three females, were by now, swept away by the comedic tragedy of his journey when we were rudely jolted out of our reverie when the actor suddenly jumped out of character. He gazed sternly over our heads towards the back of the hall.

'Excuse me, can I help you?' he asked in a rather clipped and formal voice.

We swung around and were immediately confronted by a group of male recovering alcoholics on route to their AA meeting staring dumbfounded at the sight of a seven-foot penis hopping around the stage – half of which, I suspect, had decided they must be experiencing return episodes of the DTs or at least some weird hallucination linked painfully and inexplicably to the very core of their masculinity.

The expression on their faces was priceless and, I suspect, in today's snowflake parlance, would have been grounds to charge the playwright with inflicting emotional, and possible sexual trauma on men. #SheToo (or #HeToo). Oh, how times have changed.

Opening night loomed and I decided, perhaps rather unwisely, to invite Beautiful Bad Boy to opening night. The festival was sold out and I had plus one, but as the occasion grew closer I found myself avoiding telling him what the actual theme of the play was – vague mumblings about an exploration into masculinity, clown suit, sexual satire (kept that one genderless), a return to bawdy comedy, a transgressive one-man show, anything but the actual visuals Beautiful Bad Boy was going to be presented with on the night.

I should have really thought this out a little more. I mean, it takes an awfully confident man to be the arm candy of an older female playwright who's written a play starring a seven-foot penis. Not to mention the actual theme of the play – male porn star suddenly realises he could no longer perform without emotional intimacy – not exactly my less than average friend with benefits problem was it? So not the best date night, right? Plus I started to worry about whether he'd see the scale of the penis as a statement about me being a size queen. The actor's height was an innocent coincidence but he was about seven foot once inside the costume, were some men going to be intimidated?

Finally the night arrived, and I was sitting in the auditorium, with him beside me, in a packed house, somewhere between really nervous and seriously curious as to how it would all go down.

The curtain rose in darkness. A follow spot hit on the penis, centre stage, crumpled and rolled mournfully into its testicles (head and face hidden). An eerie silence rippled through the audience, a kind of momentary suspended shock as if they were all wondering how to react. But then slowly but surely the penis unfurled into its full seven-foot height and the actor's face peeked out from between the glans. Everyone – male, female, straight, gay and everything between cracked up.

The audience absolutely loved it. The actor was superb, and the play was poignant and moving as well as deeply comedic. My only criticism was that if anything, at times, the physical comedy threatened to upstage the bathos of emotional journey of the character himself.

However it did leave some men uncomfortable. One close male friend verbally attacked me afterwards for setting unrealistic standards for the perfect penis. He had an argument, but the costume designer had designed the costume not me. The dictates of the cosmetically perfect penis were not part of the theme nor the plot (although you'd think a porn star might be required to have a good looking penis).

The journey was metaphoric – albeit delivered in a literal satirical manner – but a talking emoting penis is a talking emoting penis (not quite Gertrude Stein but you get my point). Still, I should have realised how it might have been a trigger for some less confident members of the audience.

The play was a hit and I won best comedic short. But Beautiful Bad Boy was very silent and a little awkward afterwards.

And the next morning after rolling back onto the pillow he dumped me. My heart was broken, for a few weeks anyhow. I still have the costume somewhere.

ANTHONY DIPIETRO
The Violinist at the Pulitzer Reading

a world-class male violinist either needs
   a big dick from which his confidence springs
or a small one for which he's compensating.

   tonight's violinist and pianist
climb the side stage stairs, take seats where they
   can't see each other, then begin, as one,

they play nimbly, in synch, a single melody.
   the pianist's serious, polish face;
   violinist in jeans, gray vest, red beard.

the way he holds his instrument, I know
he fancies women, and his jeans tell me
   he's large, not small. his whole upper body

   plays only for me, legs and neck kept still.
he's teaching me a lesson, how music's
a miracle he extracts from muscle

   memory. red thing in his hands, he lulls
an infant to sleep. is this music, I ask,
   breath of violin or bow? I know

   it must be the dance of two. I turn
to embrace a spectacled stranger
in a sweater at my left, eyes wet, face

sculptural, nearest handsome man in this
    panorama, unlikely trio or
    trinity—pianist, violinist,

stranger. flesh floods the temple full of allegro
(rapid) tune like fluttering feathers. lucent
    strings, piano sweet. composer nowhere in sight.

BENTON LENZ
A Hard Look

I look down
And wish I could say I was proud

Like an old friend
Maybe my oldest
I know everything about
But still don't completely understand

Or the sibling that was always around
Planting ideas in my head
Things I knew I wasn't ready for
But did anyway just to keep up

Better yet, a teenage dream maker
That took my awkwardness in stride
Begged me not to stop
And delivered me to a place that felt so good
Life had meaning

Shy. Sensitive. Insistent. Insatiable.
I learned to be very careful with introductions
And not to predict preferences
Better to be surprised

Like on my first double dates
Where the more confident one
Gave me away
But also walked me home

Or the courageous one
Who stood right up
And called it love
Right from the start

Who with a glance or a breath
Or a smell or a flicker
Would boldly revive love
Even when I was sure it was dead

And now years later
It's comforting to still know
We can play at being young again
Or just hang out and relax

Looking down
I still wish I could be proud
So instead I look up
At an aging face
In a mirror

And smile

DREW PISARRA
Sonnet 6"

Hey shlong, listen up. Hey penis, pay attention.
Pecker! Turn your unblinking eye over here.
Oh, thick-headed prick, oh tool of no pretension,
oh wood that could, and dick shaped like a can of beer.
I have ogled and gagged. I have ridden such cock.
I now testify to shafts fat and thin that assume
import for an hour then become standard stock.
Some were memorable, some not. But as to you
and yours divine which had given me such pleasure,
I had hoped to make it mine. Yet I had to let
it go. Neither you nor your manhood would measure
up to my far-flung desires. So what don't you get?
Like your dick, our love didn't prove to be that deep
but even shallow love lost can feel bittersweet.

THOM SCHWARZ
The Clinical Cock

I never saw a penis, other than my own, until I was fourteen years old while attending high school. I was a tall, thin geek, wholly unathletic and I discovered in my freshman year in the gymnasium locker room laughingly, poorly endowed. Sneaking peeks at my classmates in the showers I was immediately embarrassed by the paucity of my pecker. Already six foot four in my freshman year I knew that I had finished my adolescent growth spurt; no hope for one last surge in the penis department. Worse yet, everyone else in the boy's locker room noticed my junk, too. I became the butt of four years of rude jokes. To make matters worse some highly observant fellow saw that I had only one testicle. You mean I'm supposed to have *two*? Isn't one enough? Good grief.

Years later I worked as an orderly in the operating suite of a local hospital. I made friends with many of the nurses and surgeons. Still a virgin, I took a urologist not much older than myself into my confidence. Could a guy with a little bitty thingy and only one nut get a girl pregnant? "You don't need a crowbar to do precision work," he laughed, "that's why God gave men fingers and a tongue."

I was innocently oblivious of the meaning of this cock koan but encouraged nonetheless. Then he handed me a small plastic cup and asked for a sperm specimen. *That* I knew I could accomplish in a flash. A few days later he caught up with me to present the results. "Oh, don't worry about being potent, you're way ahead of most men in that department. Size isn't everything, remember." Easy for him to say, he was a swarthy little Italian whose surgical scrubs did little to hide his endowment.

One of my tasks as an O.R. orderly was to shave the patients on the evening before their surgery. I shaved heads, faces, arms, abdomens, and many men's crotches. (Keep in mind this was the mid-1970s, there were nurses to address the hirsute female patients' parts prior to surgery.) It seemed as though every man within 100 miles was having his hernia repaired. At first I was embarrassed and held their dicks as though they might break. But after a while it was a case of 'You've held one, you've held 'em all.' The patients were more embarrassed than I was. I kept up a continuous, banal, and hopefully distracting patter as I applied my razor round and round their peckers.

But a guy can't help noticing anatomical, and sometimes pathological, differences among all those dongs. Some were distinctly bent this way and others t'other way. Some had pointed little helmets while others had a bulbous mushroom. Some were freckled, some tanned. (How'd *that* happen?) Some were remarkably long and some familiarly stubby. None seemed to respond gaily to my attention and maneuvers to shave them back to infantile baldness. The surgeons would have me on the carpet the next day if I skimped in my ministrations to their patients' pubics.

One evening I was sent to shave a 10-year-old African American boy before his approaching hernia repair. He lay still as a statue in his bed, the white sheet pulled up to his eyes that were wide with fear. I tried to allay his fear as I set out my basin and fresh blades. Then the reveal. I was astounded. His cock was the size of the proverbial baby's

133

arm holding an apple. It *was* the size of his arm! Lord knows that little boy had a cock many times the size of mine. Lucky lad, says I.

Another extremely common procedure that I witnessed was called the cystoscopy, flexible or rigid. It was used to directly visualize a gentleman's bladder by inserting a device, a rigid or flexible tube barely smaller than the diameter of the urethra—the hole in the end of your dick—up, up, up into the bladder. Yes, there was anesthesia and sedatives involved. I felt like I needed some myself after I first witnessed a cysto. I had sympathy pains in my pecker for days.

But it could get worse for my male patients and their playthings, and through 40-plus years as a registered nurse I witnessed some gad-awful tragedies, some near and some full-blown.

One winter afternoon a teenage hockey player was brought to my emergency department by his frightened parents. He'd noticed an irritation on his nuts the prior evening but thought it nothing more serious than standard 'jock itch'. But it spread rapidly and painfully. He was forced to forgo the next day's game due to fiery pain. His parents had never seen such a ferocious, fast-moving infection. Neither had I but as the triage nurse I recognized the signs and symptoms of an uncommon but lethal bacterial infection—necrotizing fasciitis, or 'flesh-eating disease' that was fast threatening his cock, and his very life. I pulled the E.R. doc on duty out of another examination room where he was working up a patient with a far more benign problem and hustled him into the young athlete's room. Twenty minutes later the boy was riding in a medi-vac helicopter to a regional medical center. I heard they saved his cock, and his life.

Not so with another sad young man. In the early 1980s an Asian family—they turned out to be Vietnamese whereas I typically cared for the neighborhood's Central and South Americans—filed into the Manhattan hospital emergency department where I was nightly occupied in trying to save the neighborhood's overdose and gang war victims. This group spoke not a word, English or otherwise, as they approached my triage desk. I scanned the crowd of anxious eyes for someone who might be a spokesperson or the unlucky patient. No such luck. No one was bleeding, pale and diaphoretic, or raving incoherently. So far so good. I smiled and asked the magic questions: "What seems to be the problem? How can I help you?" The man who appeared the eldest stepped forward and said in a near whisper of perfect English, "Sir, my grandson needs to see a doctor."

"Okay," I replied, taking the bait. "Which one is your grandson?"

The man turned to his family and made a subtle hand motion, like Moses parting the Red Sea. The family stepped aside and two women escorted a teenage boy towards me. It was not long after the end of the war in Vietnam but as a conscientious objector who never served in the military I had never met a Vietnamese person face-to-face. His expression was both pained and inscrutable.

I brought the young man into an examination room and asked him to undress while I asked the pro forma health history questions, ending with, "What brings you to my attention tonight? What's bothering you?"

Two women had accompanied him, one of whom I suspected was his mother. I was absolutely unschooled in Vietnamese health care culture and traditions so I let the

135

women join us unchallenged. The boy lay supine on the gurney, motionless, eyes tightly shut. I asked again, "What's wrong with him?"

One woman stepped forward and gingerly pulled the sheet down to the patient's upper thighs. How I managed not to faint or gasp, "Holy shit!" is beyond me. His penis was covered, obscured, lost in a tumor the size, shape, color and texture of a full-grown cauliflower. Tiny rivulets of blood and sero-sanguinous fluid oozed from multiple crevices in the tumor. I took a breath and asked quietly, "Do you have pain?" My question was translated in a whisper. The boy shook his head. How in God's name could he *not* be in some sort of pain? And how could he have waited so long to seek help? How did he urinate? I asked a few more questions, recorded his vital signs, and explained that I would fetch a physician to begin helping him—how, I hadn't a clue.

It dawned on me later that this family, so recently escaped from their war-torn homeland and relocated in the land of their former enemy, might have hesitated long and hard before seeking such embarrassing and intricate help. Perhaps they had no insurance or financial resources. Maybe there was some other reason for their delay that I had no way of knowing. Like most emergency patients his care and eventual outcome were lost to me. My role was to help save and stabilize them and then pass them on to the next level of clinicians. In the end I wished him well as he was taken upstairs to the surgical suite for further evaluation and treatment. As I drove home that night I couldn't help but thank God for my small but happy dick and my single but fully functional testicle.

JULIANNE INGLES
We're So Sorry

There were five guys from Kuwait who called me once. I've forgotten all of their names, one might have been Mohammed and one Abdul, but I really don't remember. They had the white headscarves with the black band around the top. Teacher where are you from? they said. And then I told them where I was from and that I'd lived in Saudi and then they laughed because they couldn't believe I'd lived there and then someone's cousin came in the room and someone handed him the phone and he said – Teacher I want to sing to you. And I said ok, and then he started singing – *Help, I need somebody, help not just anybody, help!* And I laughed and said – Hey let's all sing it together – because I thought that would be funny but apparently that wasn't funny because then they hung up.

There were a lot of hang-ups with this job. And a lot of reading between the lines. Them the mischievous young Arab men, me the blonde American English teacher, all of us blank canvases. And why did they hang up? I don't know, maybe because they knew they'd crossed a line and felt embarrassed and it became too real when I said – Hey let's all sing – and that was just too much and then it was all over. And I didn't have a minute to even think about it because then another call came in. It was funny because it was like working for the phone company and I just kept answering and answering the phone.

Hi! How are you? That's how I always started out. Sometimes I waved. Sometimes I didn't. Then if no one answered I typed into the messaging box: Hello! And then sometimes someone answered and typed back and said: I can't hear you! And then I'd say: I can't hear you either! And there were all kinds of technical issues and I guess it is a pretty sophisticated thing to put together a website for English lessons with a live feed and texting and all of that, and usually it worked pretty well but lots of times it didn't.

After a while I just knew this would just happen, that screens would go black, or sound would go out, and that there wasn't really anything I could do but sit there and keep saying – Hi! How are you? Can you hear me? – and wait until someone said something or hung up. Sometimes we had really long interesting conversations, if they spoke enough English. I'm a great conversationalist and can keep it going even if the person is boring as hell, but most of the time they weren't, they just wanted to speak English and talk to a native speaker and occasionally be corrected but mostly they just wanted to talk.

Some of them wanted to know about me, like there was one guy from Saudi Arabia who wanted to know my life story. That was after I stupidly told him I was a memoirist. Stupid because I really shouldn't have told anyone anything personal about myself at all because you never know what kind of creeps are out there. Anyway, I was knee deep into this and this guy kept asking for my life story so finally I told him. It was the abbreviated version with simple verbs and graded language. It went something like this: I was born in Chicago. I grew up Catholic. I went to Catholic school for nine years. Then I went to a public high school. Then I went to college and studied art. Then I became an artist. Then later I became a writer.

It was funny, because even as boring as that is, the guy

just lapped it up and kept asking questions, like he'd stop me and say – How many years did you go to Catholic school? And I'd say nine. And then he'd ask me what I studied at Catholic school and I'd have to explain that it was all the normal subjects you would study anywhere except that we studied religion too, and the whole time I was telling this guy my life story he was walking around the streets of Riyadh, dusty cement streets, I don't think I saw even one tree, it's funny that anyone would think of building a monstrous city like that in the middle of the hottest driest desert in the world, but they did and I didn't miss it one bit, and I guess I didn't mind telling this guy my life story because he was such a good listener.

Anyway, there were tons of guys like this. The picture I had on my profile was nice, I suppose nice is an accurate word. Nice and young. It was taken about 10 years ago. Anyway, so a lot of Middle Eastern guys called me, and flirted with me, and I didn't really care because it seemed so harmless. The Turkish guys called too. I've never really been sure what part of the world that is, I mean it's not really the Middle East and it's not really Europe, so I don't really know what to call it other than Turkey, some vague distant place lingering in cyberspace.

I had one guy who was Turkish and he was living in Brighton doing an intensive English course for a few months. He was really nice, I mean we talked every day for about a week and each time it was about forty-five minutes and he kept making reservations for lessons and I guess it all seemed pretty harmless even though I knew he was married and knew he was interested in me. He'd say things like – I really like that sweater you're wearing, what color is that? And I'd say lavender and he'd go on for a minute or so about how nice it looked on me and I'd say – Oh, I usually wear black, that's my color – and I suppose it was flattering and I suppose I liked the attention, but anyway it was pretty obvious that he was interested.

One day when we were practicing questions he started saying – How long does it take to get from Brighton to London? And I just kind of ignored it and said I don't really know. Because I don't think I told you this but I live in London and this guy knew I lived in London and Brighton is only about an hour away by train, and so when he said that I decided to blow it off because if I paid any attention at all to this it would have been weird. Weird, like an acknowledgment of the weirdness of it and a busting down of boundaries because we were in this bubble-like cyber world that seemed safe and I liked it how it was and then finally we stopped practicing questions and he didn't ask that again. But later, on another day when we were talking about Islam and I asked him how many times a day he prayed and he said five, then we started talking and talking about the Muslim religion in great detail and how some things are different in different countries, and how the guys from Saudi Arabia covered their cameras because they weren't supposed to be talking to a woman, but they all pray five times a day and I think this guy really liked it that I'd taken an interest in his religion, and then we started talking about some book and I can't remember the name of the book but it was something about Islam and he said – If you send me your address, I'll send it to you.

That was when it started to feel creepy. So I said – Oh you know what I'm moving next week. That's what I said because I was moving, and because obviously I didn't want to give him my address. So I said – I'll give you my new address after I move – which I didn't intend for a minute to do because again it was this awkward moment and I didn't like all the pushing this guy was doing and then he said – So you're moving? And I said – Yeah, this weekend. I'll take a few days off. And he said – But you'll be back next week? And I said – Yeah, I'll be back next week.

A few days later I had a reservation with one of my regular students, Ayah. She was Syrian but living in Jeddah because of the war. I think it was our second lesson and we followed one of those pre-made lesson plans and this one was about living abroad, and what kind of challenges there are, and how it takes time to adjust to a new culture and the food and the people and all that kind of stuff. It was fun to talk to Ayah. She was 28 and sweet and reserved and wouldn't say a bad thing about anyone. She smiled a lot and talked about her children and how she wanted to learn English so she could help them learn. And it was nice that she didn't cover her camera, almost all of the women from Saudi covered their camera and I ended up staring at a black screen, but Ayah was different. I could see her face, and her head was wrapped in a patterned pale blue scarf that she kept tucking behind her ear. It was very easy to talk to Ayah because she was so sweet and angelic and I'd lived in the Middle East for three years so I knew what kind of things to talk about.

The conversation went on for about an hour, then we said goodbye and then another call came in and the screen was black and I kept saying – Hello! How are you? Hello, hello! Until finally I saw a black and white checked shirt and then the camera started moving around like they were getting situated, and so I waited a few seconds and stared at the screen and the moving camera as it scrolled down and down to the man's crotch, his hand grasping his erect penis, sliding up and down and up and down and up and down.

Oh god this isn't happening. Oh shit this is disgusting what the fuck kind of fucking pervert called me? Jesus fucking hell, what the fuck?

I hit the report/ban this student button, the button that was on the screen for every call, and the call disconnected.

A number of windows and empty boxes popped up on the screen and I was asked to explain what had happened. Reeling with shock, brain blank, not knowing what the hell just happened or what to do next, I answered their questions like this: Indecent exposure and masturbation, that's why the fuck I'm reporting this fuck-wad you sent me.

Then, as if this were protocol or just so typical that they had a system in place, a window opened up and said: Now take a 10-minute break. Or, you can be released from your priority hour without penalty.

I clicked on 'take a 10 minute break' and stood up dazed and foggy and trying to shake the image of that guy's dick and his hand stroking it from my mind and went outside on the balcony to smoke a cigarette. Take a 10-minute break? Some guy fucking plows his way into my face and shoves his camera in his crotch and starts masturbating and what do I get – TAKE A 10 MINUTE BREAK! Fuck, it was so fucked up, that was all I could think.

I walked back to my computer and saw from a distance what had happened, some horrible car crash, and it began to sink in and I took two more calls, short ones, but couldn't keep up the conversations and each time I answered I kept thinking, god it could be that same pervert and then I got through the second call and logged off. Then I sent an email to the company and told them what had happened and that it was fucked up and that I was cancelling for the rest of the week and didn't know if I would ever come back.

While I was waiting for their reply, I clicked around on the pervert's profile and found his preferred language: Turkish. Was it the guy from Brighton using a fake name? I suppose it could have been but he didn't seem like a pervert, then again what is a pervert like when they're not being perverted? And of course Turkey was a big country and it could've been anyone and the whole account and profile was probably fake and did he know that he was being recorded? Was that even a consideration? Or part of the thrill? I really didn't know anything.

And why do men do this? What the fuck is the thrill of forcing a woman to stare at you while you masturbate? Why is it that women don't do shit like this? Would you ever see a woman do something like that? I doubt it though I suppose anything's possible but I have a hard time imagining a woman spreading her legs and pointing a camera at it and forcing someone to stare at her. Unless she was a porn star. But why would a porn star be trying to learn English? Wouldn't she rather be on a porn site getting paid to have people stare at her?

A long time ago when I was in college I was sitting in my car and it was late at night and I was parked on a side street and I was fumbling around getting situated when I heard someone tap on the passenger's window. Tap tap tap. It took a minute for me to look up because it was such a light tap and when I did look there was this guy with his pants down masturbating with his dick about an inch away from the window. I was pretty freaked out because it was late at night and no one else was around and I didn't know where my keys were, so I started digging through my purse and by the time I found my keys and started the engine the guy had come on the window, a thick spatter of yellowish white disgustingness. Then I drove off. And the funny thing was that he knocked. Because it wasn't good enough to be masturbating in public, someone had to see. I had to see. Just like the Turkish guy. And I wonder what he did after I disconnected the call or if he even knew I disconnected the call or if he was watching me, yes of course he was watching me, one hand holding his phone and one hand holding his dick all the while leaning back on his bed and what an acrobatic feat to do such a thing. Yes of course he was watching me watch him for all of five or ten seconds, and what was the plan he had in mind? Like do they think this all the way through and imagine what it will be like afterwards? Did that even cross his mind? Did he think I would say something or send him my phone number or scream or pull my clothes off and say – Oh god you are so fucking hot. Maybe it was more like an alcoholic taking a drink, unable to stop, knowing they shouldn't but doing it anyway, and on and on I tried to imagine what the fuck the guy was thinking and what would possess him to do such a thing and why he thought, or thinks, that he wouldn't get caught.

The thing is that I don't know who it was. It could've been the guy from Brighton even though he seemed nice and I had no reason to believe he was anything other than nice but then again how does anyone know what another person is really like? I mean one minute a person can be completely appropriate and the next minute dropping their pants and pulling their dick out and masturbating. No one really knows anything and that's what bothered me. I wanted to know, and I needed to know who the hell it was. The company wasn't much help and that bothered me too. They were in San Francisco. And when they replied to my email they said they were really sorry and that they were doing everything they could to keep people like this off their platform and how very sad and deeply disturbing that something like this could happen to one of their 'dear teachers'.

It went something like that, and then they said – Although this doesn't make up for what happened, we have added one hour's pay to your account. Ten dollars and seventeen cents. And when it finally began to sink in what had happened and how fucked up it was and that no one was going to do anything about it, I started to get pissed off. And then I replied to their email and asked to speak with someone on the phone. A day later they replied – We're very sorry but we don't have the resources to talk to our teachers on the phone. But don't hesitate to get in touch by email!

It was pretty infuriating. They had the guy's IP address. They had his email address. And they had the incident on video. Because they recorded all the lessons. And it occurred to me that this probably wasn't the first time something like this had happened. And they were washing their hands of it, washing and washing and scrubbing their filthy hands. And that really pissed me off.

So, I called the San Francisco police and asked to file a report and they said they had to do it in person and if I wasn't there in San Francisco then I'd have to go to the local police in my area, which is what I did. And it's funny how the British police are, meaning very British and proper as hell and how they don't like to say the word masturbate, so I was really blunt and told the story about three times until the lady behind the glass window finally got someone to fill out a report for me and she started to explain that – Someone exposed himself to her and he was – and then there was this uncomfortable pause as she stared at me and so I finished her sentence and said – masturbating – because she couldn't seem to bring herself to say the word. I don't know, what the hell else was I supposed to do. Then the guy who was writing the report asked a million questions like what the guy looked like and I laughed and said I only saw his penis and his hand and the man said – Oh, I see – and kept typing up the report until finally when he was almost finished he said – If the suspect is caught would you like to press charges? And I said – Yes.

Because it was real, and he was real, and I was real, and the whole fucking thing needed to be acknowledged as real, really fucking real, really fucking perverted, really fucking fucked up, as much as anything is real, and as much as I know that it doesn't always feel very real when I see someone on a screen, more like an episode of *The Jetsons* back in the day when no one ever thought it even remotely possible that you'd be able to see and talk to someone on a television screen, science fiction at its height, of course that could never happen, but it did happen, and does happen and of course it's real, real as can be, real pixels connected to real people, people who are sometimes complete perverts, or people who own companies who recruit English teachers without the slightest mention of the possibility of a dick being thrust in their face while performing their job, people who gasp and balk as if this has never happened before, people who click and type and shoot off pathetic emails, conveniently hidden away in some posh office in San

Francisco, as they say: We're so sorry!

KATHLEEN A LAWRENCE
Too Many to Count

I think I saw my first sprawled
across the natty cloth seat
of a neighbor's Rambler,
a shocking deflated balloon animal
laying wrinkled and uninspired
waiting for something,
I didn't know what,
but it obviously needed something
I didn't know why it was there,
on the front seat,
that humid July afternoon
but I quickly knew to look away,
feeling my freckles hot,
and my cheeks flush, I learned
quickly, and it wouldn't be long,
maybe a couple of years
before another gentleman
(that's what I was taught to call
any male over 20)
showed me his on the downtown bus
to see the Christmas display
in Midtown Plaza,
although I didn't want it,
I got a much better look at his
and it seemed to stare back
at me across the aisle
like a creepy cyclops

then one time I took my younger
siblings to the playground
and as I watched them climbing
the monkey bars and swinging to the sky
an officer approached to warn me
that I should tell him if I saw anyone
doing anything illegal, nervous
from my unexpected assignment,
but eager to show respect to the law,
I looked but all I could imagine
was bank robbers with kerchiefs
over their faces, holding derringers,
demanding bags be filled with money,
not man-sacks
but before he walked away
I realized the zipper on his regulation
navy slacks was down
and his partner was out
for all of us to see
once I was at the country club
and four teenage boys dropped
their swim trunks to show me
their shriveled underwater sea creatures
as I passed the locker room
and I tried to look away quickly,
but not before Dan took his in hand
and waved it at me like a flag in a parade.

It seemed to me that no matter
where I went I might see one,
and my life has continued
to be dotted with a series of sightings,

mostly uninvited and not encouraged,
too many to remember,
but too many to forget either,
as they came like a salty wave
that surprises you while standing
innocently on a beautiful shore
disrupting the view
and interrupting the moment,
one shock of icy water I got
was from the dad of a little boy
I was babysitting, for while taking me
back home in the family wagon,
he reeked of whiskey and sleaze
in his polyester slacks when he asked me
if I wanted to see it or even touch it,
I declined the offer, getting out quickly
with my pay of 75 cents per hour,
turned out he was cheap and crude
and then one wintry afternoon
I was ice skating at Ellison park
when I sashayed past a man
sitting on a bench who I discovered
was holding his thing up
with his brown Isotoner gloves,
he smirked as I almost lost
my balance at the sight
like a troll under the bridge,
he was so pleased with himself
that he had disrupted my idyllic pastime,
and yes, there was a time
(or two or three) in college,
like when I came back from the bathroom

and my study partner was standing naked
in my dorm room having removed
his button-fly jeans to "Jumpin' Jack Flash",
he grinned explaining he was just waiting
for me to return to memorize
formulas for my math final,
why not be comfortable? he asked,
and much like my professor, in his office,
who wanted to be sure I understood
the importance of registering early
for Spring semester,
he was so thoughtful to keep it behind
his polished mahogany desk
while advising me
and there were at least a baker's dozen
of my trips on the subway, mostly the D Train
that seemed to be ripe with men
baring unwanted fruit for other weary travelers
and swimming one starless summer night
when half the guys went underwater
only to come up waving their cut-off shorts
that they had ceremoniously removed
and then one time I remember,
in my graduate dorm
a guy was sneaking into rooms
and putting his thing
like a receiver through the phone box
between the two rooms, he also might
have been the guy who hung
around the women's shower
or streaked the tenth floor—girls' side,
oh, I've seen them on buses, too,

and on the great NYS Thruway
between Geneva and Canandaigua
when I guess some guy
and his buddy thought I cut them off,
so they decided to show me
by flipping me their birds
and like many women I've seen them
in the elegant New York Public Library,
despite the stately stone lions
guarding the books outside
and in lovely hotel lobbies,
why, I saw one just last year
at a conference on rhetorical exigencies,
and there have been sightings
in posh restaurants, and at fundraisers,
and wine tastings, and at the gym,
work, outside, inside, upstairs, downstairs,
anywhere and everywhere, so many,
too many to mention all of them here
and I'm getting older now,
and not recalling all of them,
but despite my six decades of living,
and my general disinterest,
they just keep on coming, a sad army
of unwanted soldiers limping home.

CONTRIBUTORS

Matt Dennison (Columbus, MS, USA)

After a rather extended and varied second childhood in New Orleans, Matt Dennison's work has appeared in *Rattle*, *Bayou Magazine*, *Redivider*, *Natural Bridge*, *The Spoon River Poetry Review* and *Cider Press Review*, among others. He has also made short films with Michael Dickes, Swoon, Marie Craven and Jutta Pryor.

Gerry Marsh (London)

Gerry Marsh's previous writing successes have included a book of short stories entitled *Tales of Urban Encounters* (2018, available on Amazon). She has also written 'Self', an article in *Therapy Today* (2016), was a finalist in One Stop Stories Valentine Competition (2014), has written articles for the *Guardian* (2012), and was a finalist in the Welsh One Act Play Competition (1999). In 2017, she graduated from MA in Creative Writing from University of Kent. She has just finished writing *Flight of the Dodo*. For info: www.gerrymarsh.co.uk.

Catherine Edmunds (Bishop Auckland, UK)

Catherine Edmunds is a prolific writer, artist, and fiddle player with award nominated Irish folk/rock band 'Share the Darkness'. Her published written works include two poetry collections, four novels and a Holocaust memoir. She has been nominated three times for a Pushcart Prize, shortlisted in the Bridport four times, and has works in journals including *Aesthetica*, *Crannóg* and *Ambit*. Catherine lives in

North-East England between the High Pennines and the Grey North Sea.

Ann Rawson (Brighton, UK)
Ann Rawson's debut novel, *A Savage Art*, inspired by her love of textile arts and dark fairy tales, was published by Fahrenheit Press in 2016. Her first short story, 'A Dog's Life', will appear in *Me Too Stories* edited by Elizabeth Zelvin and published by Level Best Books. Another piece, 'If...', was shortlisted for the Fish Short Memoir prize 2019. Although she still thinks of herself as a Northerner, she lives near Brighton with her husband and an elderly cat who accompanies them on their walks. She is currently working on a full-length memoir.

Adem Ay (London)
Adem Ay is a London based writer and filmmaker who has been struggling to write a competent feature film for ten years. That dishevelled guy in the cafe with the laptop and the cold cup of coffee - that's him. He's still going. To stay alive he writes short films for NGOs, a blog for a film website, and hosts his own pub quizzes.

Liam Hogan (London)
Liam Hogan is an Oxford Physics graduate whose award winning short story, 'Ana', appears in *Best of British Science Fiction 2016* (NewCon Press). 'The Dance of a Thousand Cuts' appears in *Best of British Fantasy 2018*. He lives and avoids work in London. More details at http://happyendingnotguaranteed.blogspot.co.uk

Alex Carrigan (Alexandria, VA, USA)

Alex Carrigan is an assistant editor with the American Correctional Association. He has edited and proofed the anthologies *CREDO: An Anthology of Manifestos and Sourcebook for Creative Writing* (C&R Press, 2018) and *Her Plumage: An Anthology of Women's Writings from Quail Bell Magazine* (forthcoming 2019). He has had fiction, poetry, and media reviews published in *Quail Bell Magazine, Life in 10 Minutes, Realms YA Fantasy Literary Magazine, Mercurial Stories, Lambda Literary Review* and the forthcoming anthology *Closet Cases: LGBTIQ Writers on What We Wear* (Et Alia Press, April 2020). He currently lives in Alexandria, VA.

Gayelene Carbis (Melbourne, Australia)

Gayelene Carbis is an award-winning writer of poetry, prose and plays from Melbourne. Her first book of poetry, *Anecdotal Evidence* (Five Islands Press), was awarded finalist in the 2019 International Book Awards for Poetry, sponsored by American Book Fest. Other shortlistings / prizes include: MPU International Poetry Prize; *Meniscus* Best Small Fiction; Fish Memoir Prize; Fish Short Story Prize (Ireland); and the Montreal International Poetry Prize, as well as various short story awards. Gayelene has read her work in Australia and internationally, including Canada, New York, Egypt and Greece. Gayelene teaches Creative Writing at various universities. She is currently teaching English/EAL and working as Writer-in-Residence (Poetry) in a school.

Christina Lovin (Lancaster, KY, USA)

Christina Lovin's prose and poetry has appeared in over one hundred different literary journals and anthologies, as well as five volumes of poetry (*Echo, A Stirring in the Dark, Flesh, Little Fires,* and *What We Burned for Warmth*). She is the recipient of numerous poetry awards, writing residencies, fellowships and grants, most notably the Al Smith Fellowship from Kentucky Arts Council, Kentucky Foundation for Women Artist Enrichment Grant, and an Elizabeth George Foundation Grant.

Thaddeus Rutkowski (New York)
Thaddeus Rutkowski is the author of six books, most recently *Border Crossings*, a poetry collection. His novel *Haywire* won the Asian American Writers' Workshop's members' choice award, and his memoir *Guess and Check* won the Electronic Literature bronze award for multicultural fiction. He received a fiction writing fellowship from the New York Foundation for the Arts.

Edward Apeldoorn (Netherlands)
Edward Apeldoorn lives in a very old brick house with his wife and an unknown number of cats. His writing has been rejected by many of the finest publications in the world. His penis is extravagantly average.

Shringi Kumari (London)
A drifter, Shringi likes to think, express and ask. She uses Madhubani paintings, games, writing and dance as a medium to bare layered nuances. Her writings root from thoughts held in thin air, observations made in private and an endless pursuit of self. She and her art are rather abstract and invite interpretation. Shringi has been working in game development for the past 12 years and is now doing a PhD in the same field.

Sarah Evans (Welwyn Garden City, UK)

Sarah Evans has had many short stories published in anthologies, literary journals and online. She has been shortlisted by the Commonwealth Short Story Prize and been awarded prizes by, amongst others: Words and Women, Stratford Literary Festival and the Bridport Prize. Her work is also included in several *Unthology* volumes, *Best New Writing* and *Shooter Magazine*.

Molly McLellan (Invermere BC, Canada)

Molly McLellan is a research nut to say the least. It never seems to fail that her pieces of fiction always end up leading her down the endless rabbit hole of sources, upon sources, upon sources. Perhaps this is why she felt the need to obtain a master's degree from Oxford in Creative Writing. Combining her two great loves of research and writing fiction in a place with one of the world's largest libraries and oldest collection of books. Now back home in Canada, she spends her days working at a local art gallery and cultural center known as Pynelogs when she's not writing or out adventuring with her beloved dog Jack.

Tobsha Learner (London)

Tobsha Learner is an author of historical fiction, thrillers and erotic fiction. Books include the bestsellers *Quiver* (erotic fiction) *Sphinx* (as TS Learner) and *The Witch of Cologne* (historical fiction). *The Magick Of Master Lilly*, her 11th book, was published by Little Brown UK, 2018. She is also a playwright and screenwriter. For info: www.tobsha.com.

Anthony DiPietro (Cambridge, MA, USA)

Anthony DiPietro is a gay writer and Rhode Island native who spent his career in community-based organizations and now serves as associate director of the Rose Art Museum near Boston. While earning his MFA at Stony Brook, he also taught undergraduate courses, planned readings and campus events, and helped diversify programming. His poems and essays appear in *Notre Dame Review*, *Spillway*, *The American Poetry Journal*, and many others. During his two years as a graduate student, he was named a finalist with four literary journals and awarded fellowships to attend three writing seminars and three residencies. His website is AnthonyWriter.com.

Benton Lenz (Union Pier, MI, USA)

Benton Lenz is a versatile creative professional with 35 years of writing, painting, art direction and graphic design experience. He maintains creative studios in Austin, Texas and southwest Michigan.

Drew Pisarra (New York)

Brooklynite Drew Pisarra is one half of Saint Flashlight, a poetry activation duo with Molly Gross that finds inventive ways of getting verse into public spaces. *Infinity Standing Up*, his first book of poems, was released by Capturing Fire press in early 2019. *Publick Spanking*, his collection of short stories, was released by Future Tense eons ago.

Thom Schwarz (Pleasant Valley, NY, USA)

Thom Schwarz RN, lives in the Hudson River valley of New York State, U.S. He has been a published writer since he was 11 years old. His work has been in the *New York*

Times Magazine, The Journal of the American Medical Association, Newsweek, and many magazines and newspaper columns. This is his premier piece to be published about his, and others', penis.

Julianne Ingles (London)

A Chicago native, Julianne Ingles is a painter, writer, editor and founder of Guts Publishing. Her degrees include an MA in Creative & Life Writing and an MA in Modern Literature, both from Goldsmiths College in London. Her websites are inglesart.com and gutspublishing.com.

Kathleen A Lawrence (Cortland, NY, USA)

Kathleen A Lawrence started writing poetry just three years ago. Since then she has had poems published in *Rattle (Poets Respond), Eye to the Telescope, Scryptic, Haikuniverse, Silver Blade Magazine, Altered Reality Magazine, Star*Line Magazine, Undertow Tanka Review, New Verse News,* among others. She has also been published in a few anthologies like *Proud to Be: Writing by American Warriors.* Recently two of her poems were nominated for 'Best of the Net' awards, and three for Rhysling Awards (SFPA), and one was nominated for a Pushcart Prize.

COPYRIGHTS FOR INDIVIDUAL TITLES

CPSIA information can be obtained
at www.ICGtesting.com
Printed in the USA
LVHW091601261119
638587LV00001B/233/P

9 781999 882327